LANGUAGE ARTS 1010
Communication Skills and Fiction Review

LIFEPAC Test is located at the back of the booklet. Please remove before starting the unit.

Author:
Mary Robbins, M.A.

Editor-in-Chief:
Richard W. Wheeler, M.A.Ed.

Editor:
Mary Ellen Quint, Ph.D.

Consulting Editor:
Larry Howard, Ed.D.

Revision Editor:
Alan Christopherson, M.S.

804 N. 2nd Ave. E.
Rock Rapids, IA 51246-1759

Communication Skills and Fiction Review

Introduction

The preceding LIFEPACs in tenth grade Language Arts present the history of English, its complex structure, its various levels of usage, its effective use, and its power in imaginative pieces of literature. You undoubtedly realize that all nine LIFEPACs are related, but perhaps you need to pull all that information into structures so that you can remember the relationships you noticed earlier. You may also need to review details. Do you remember, for example, how to form the plurals of nouns, how to read the etymology of a word, or how to prepare for an oral interpretation of a piece of literature? The information you have examined is worth understanding and remembering. You may not have the time, however, to go through the previous nine LIFEPACs exercise by exercise.

This tenth LIFEPAC® was written to help you to review the details you have forgotten and to enable you to fit together bits of knowledge until you are aware of larger, useful patterns. You will be given opportunities to test your knowledge with new exercises. You will frequently be given summaries that emphasize the important points in the material you have studied. Finally, because this review is organized somewhat differently, you will be able to exercise and combine skills repeatedly. You may even find that information that was difficult before has suddenly become easier. Think of this review as a means of enjoying and remembering valuable information.

Objectives

Read these objectives. The objectives tell you what you will be able to do when you have successfully completed this LIFEPAC. When you have finished this LIFEPAC, you will be able to:

1. Explain some words' histories and levels of meaning.

2. Spell noun plurals and suffixes.

3. Identify selected sentence elements and use them to construct coherent and concise sentences.

4. Punctuate writing to make ideas clear.

5. Explain elements of an expository essay.

6. Explain the elements of a speech.

7. Identify the elements of oral interpretation.

8. Explain necessary listening skills.

9. Identify the major points in reading material.

10. Explain some elements of poetry and interpret poems.

11. Identify the characters and structure of the drama *Everyman*.

12. Explain some elements of short stories.

13. Discuss the novel, *In His Steps*, using the skills acquired in this series.

Survey the LIFEPAC. Ask yourself some questions about this study. Write your questions here.

_____
_____
_____
_____
_____
_____
_____
_____
_____
_____
_____
_____
_____
_____
_____
_____
_____
_____

1. WRITING

Throughout history, many of the people most remembered and respected have left written records of their thoughts or transactions. In present society you must be able to write clearly and concisely in order to record business transactions, scholarly exercises or studies, and personal messages. Your manner of written expression reveals not only your message but also your level of education and your willingness (or unwillingness) to have yourself easily understood. Clearly, writing well is essential.

Yet, writing well is difficult because so many skills are involved. You must spell and form words correctly, you must arrange sentences clearly, you must construct paragraphs logically, and you must pull paragraphs together so that they work to form a unified piece of writing. All these skills require frequent review, careful examination, and, finally, practice. This section should enable you to review, to understand, and to practice writing skills.

Section Objectives

Review these objectives. When you have completed this section, you should be able to:

1. Explain some words' histories and levels of meaning.
2. Spell noun plurals and suffixes.
3. Identify selected sentence elements and use them to construct coherent and concise sentences.
4. Punctuate writing to make ideas clear.
5. Explain elements of an expository essay.

Vocabulary

Study these words to enhance your learning success in this section.

antecedent	appositive	connectives
connotation	coordinating conjunction	etymology
expository writing	illustrative	inflections
intensive	levels of usage	nonrestrictive
process analysis	reflexive	restrictive
suffix	syntax	verbal

Note: *All vocabulary words in this LIFEPAC appear in* **boldface** *print the first time they are used. If you are unsure of the meaning when you are reading, study the definitions given in the glossary.*

UNDERSTANDING AND USING WORDS

The building blocks of our language are words, units of speech that have independent meaning and are written with a space on either side. To use words effectively, you need to understand their levels of meaning and to spell them correctly so that they may be read by others.

The development of English. The history of English is interesting and useful in helping you understand features of the English language that do not seem to make sense otherwise. Chart 1 should enable you to review the major periods of English brought about by invasions, travel, and political and cultural developments. If any part of the chart is unfamiliar to you, you should review Language Arts 1001, Section 2, in more detail. Even this general outline should convince you that English as it is known today has undergone constant changes.

These historical changes have produced difficulties in English. Many words are spelled and formed as they were when they were first borrowed from other languages. Some Old English words retain spellings that made more sense when English was pronounced differently and was heavily inflected. Thus, our spelling "rules" must take into consideration the rules of many other languages at several periods of development. In addition, words have taken on new meanings as history has offered new experiences.

 Make a chart.

1.1 Use the information in the chart to the right to make a chart of your own. You may condense information or use different groupings, but you should point out in some way how English has changed. Explain your chart to your teacher.

TEACHER CHECK _____ _____
                    initials   date

CHART 1: THE HISTORY OF ENGLISH

Period	Characteristics of that Period's English	Historical Influences	English of the Period That Survived In Today's English
Old English (Anglo Saxon) AD 450-1150	The Germanic dialects of the Angles, Saxons, and Jutes became the basis for English. Several words were borrowed from Latin; some of Latin's structure was borrowed. About 1,000 words were borrowed from Old Norse.	AD 450 The Angles, Saxons, and Jutes invaded England. AD 597 Christian missionaries from Rome appeared in England. AD 787 The Danes invaded England.	83 per cent of 1,000 most frequently used words are of Old English origin. Many Latin words borrowed in that period still survive.
Middle English 1150-1475	10,000 Norman French words were added to English. The Old English inflectional endings were disappearing.	1066 The Normans, led by William the Conqueror, invaded and controlled England's government, church, and military organizations. London became an important city, and its Midland dialect became the English standard dialect.	About 7,500 French words borrowed in that period are still in use.
Early Modern English 1475-1700	The Great English Vowel Shift had occurred so that vowels were pronounced unlike those in Middle English. Portuguese, Italian, Spanish, Arabic, Latin, and Greek words were borrowed.	Trade with other countries flourished. Interest in Greek and Roman art thrived. Scientific discoveries began. Caxton printed books so that works could be quickly produced in several copies.	Most of the word borrowings still exist. Pronunciation has remained about the same.
Late Modern English 1700-1850	Dictionaries became popular as the middle class became concerned with correct English usage.	The Age of Reason industrialized England and America, and the middle class gained momentum.	Spelling and usage are similar to standards adopted then.
	Dialects other than standard London were spoken in America. Words outdated in England continued to be used in America, especially in isolated areas. Americans borrowed and coined words to name plants, animals, and new ways of living.	America was colonized and settlers moved westward.	American English has a vocabulary, and pronunciation standards different from British English.
1850-Present	Inventors and manufacturers formed thousands of new words to name and describe their products.	New inventions made mass communications, improved transportation, and assembly-line products possible.	Thousands of words have been added to our vocabularies since 1850.

Specific changes in English are outlined here. If any portion of the outline is unclear to you, review Language Arts 1001, Section 1.

I. Changes occur in vocabulary.

    A.   *Borrowed words* come from other languages.
    B.   *Coined words* come from English or foreign word elements, but are combined in new ways to form new words.
    C.   *Deletions and replacements* occur, usually because more popular synonyms have made the less popular words pass out of use.

II. Changes occur in meaning.

    A.   *Amelioration* occurs when a word becomes more and takes a more positive meaning.
    B.   *Pejoration* occurs when a word becomes less and takes a more negative meaning.
    C.   *Generalization* occurs when a word's meaning is extended beyond its original definition.
    D.   *Specialization* occurs when a word's meaning is narrowed within the boundaries of its original definition.

III. Changes occur in pronunciation and spelling.

    A.   *Dialects* (versions of language that differ in pronunciation, grammar, and vocabulary) have occurred when groups were separated by distance or social status.
    B.   *Linguistic shifts* in pronunciation (such as the *Germanic Consonant Shift* and the *Great English Vowel Shift*) have occurred.
    C.   Spelling varied according to dialect until printing began to fix certain standards.

IV. Changes occur in grammar.

    A.   *Affixes* and *bases* are constantly combined to produce new words and word groups.
    B.   **Inflections** have disappeared and a fixed word order, or **syntax**, has become more important.
    C.   The *subjunctive mood* of verbs is falling into disuse.
    D.   Auxiliary verbs have developed to indicate fine distinctions in tense and tone.

V. Changes occur in punctuation.

    A.   Punctuation has become standardized.
    B.   Sentences have become shorter and punctuation has been simplified.

 Complete this linguistic change activity.

1.2   Choose either Section 1, 2, or 4 in the preceding outline and write an example for every term of linguistic change that is printed in italics or boldface. You may need to consult Language Arts 1001, Section 1, for help, but do not use the examples given there.

TEACHER CHECK _____ _____
                                                initials   date

The following partial entry is from the *Oxford English Dictionary*.[1] Read it carefully and complete the activities that follow. If you have difficulties with the entry, the **etymology**, or any other elements review Language Arts 1004, Section 1.

Fear (fîr), sb...[OE. fær..., sudden calamity, danger, corresponds to OS. *fâr* ambush..., OHG. *fâr*, fem., ambush, stratagem, danger, ON. *fâr*,neut., misfortune, plague...]

1. obsolete: In OE.: A sudden and terrible event; peril...
2. The emotion of pain or uneasiness caused by the sense of impending danger, or by the prospect of some evil...

Write the letter of the correct answer on each line.

1.3 How do you know where to find the etymology of this word? _____
   a. It appears in parentheses.
   c. It appears after number 1.
           b. It appears in brackets.
           d. It does not appear in this entry.

1.4 What language is the source of this word? _____
   a. French
   c. Old Norse
           b. Spanish
           d. Old English

1.5 For which language does the abbreviation OHG stand? _____
   a. Old English
   c. Old Hallowed Greek
           b. Old French
           d. Old High German

1.6 The Old Saxon word far is _____ .
   a. a cognate
   c. an inflection
           b. a source
           d. a pejoration

1.7 Definition 1 is _____ .
   a. the most common definition
   c. a definition no longer used
           b. the most difficult definition
           d. the most recent definition

Answer the following question.

1.8 How has the meaning of the word *fear* changed?

_____

_____

_____

[1]Oxford English Dictionary by permission of Oxford University Press.

Label the process that each of the following words has undergone.

Use the appropriate code letter:

a. amelioration   b. pejoration   c. specialization   d. generalization

1.9 *deer*, from OE *dēor* (any four-footed wild animal)   _____

1.10 *lord*, from OE *hlāf weard* (loaf keeper)   _____

1.11 *silly*, from OE *sēlig* (happy)   _____

1.12 *nice*, from ME *nice* (foolish)   _____

1.13 *knight*, from OE *cniht* (servant)   _____

1.14 *meat*, from OE *mete* (food)   _____

1.15 *barn*, from OE *bere ærn* (barley house)   _____

Name the language from which these words were borrowed. Use a dictionary if necessary.

1.16 bigot   _____

1.17 violin   _____

1.18 insane   _____

1.19 halo   _____

1.20 volcano   _____

1.21 hamburger   _____

1.22 ranch   _____

1.23 raccoon   _____

Differences in American and British English exist. When you read something published in England, you may notice unfamiliar words, expressions, or spelling. These differences probably are not errors, but simply traits of British English. These differences have occurred because American speakers of English were unfamiliar with changes in language that were happening in Britain. Also, the words in *An American Dictionary of the English Language* (published in 1828 by the American Noah Webster) applied the simplified, American spelling, and left out the British spelling.

Some vocabulary differences between American and British English can be seen in the following lists.

American	British
pantry	larder
touchdown	try
water heater	geyser
white-collar	blackcoat
cracker	biscuit
carnival	fun fair
radio	wireless

Some spelling differences that occur between American and British English are listed.

American

-or (as in *honor*, *color*)
-er (as in *center*, *theater*)
-ow (as in *plow*)
-ize (as in *criticize*)

British

-our (as in *honour*, *colour*)
-re (as in *centre*, *theatre*)
-ough (as in *plough*)
-ise (as in *criticise*)

American regional dialects also exist. British settlers with different dialects brought their variations to America. The migration, geographic barriers causing isolation, and economic conditions causing various levels of social structure resulted in a number of American English dialects. There are so many distinct differences in language between areas of the United States that the map can be divided into 24 or more regional dialects.

Standard English **levels of usage** are all used, but the level depends on the purpose, audience, and context. Standard English reflects the widely accepted language patterns, and it is the version used in schools, writing, testing, and formal settings. The levels of usage specify differences in formality and general language rules.

Formal has no contractions; relies on elevated, scholarly words such as *terminate* rather than *end* and *facilitate* rather than *make easy*, or *capitulate* rather than *surrender*; is usually used in academic and formal writing or speaking.

Semi-formal allows some contractions, some recently formed words, but avoids excessive use of slang; is usually found in writing, work and school, and daily settings.

Informal (sometimes labeled "Colloquial") contains many contractions and some slang; has fragments sometimes replacing sentences; is used in conversations with friends, text messages, and social media.

Each level of usage is appropriate for a certain group of listeners or readers. It is important to consider your audience and purpose to make sure that your language fits your goal.

The meaning of words. The **connotations** of words may be as important to a writer as the denotations of words. The denotation of a word is its literal meaning. You have already reviewed how denotations have changed, and you should understand how important using the correct word precisely is. Yet, you must consider not only the denotation of a word, but also its connotations, its suggestive meanings, to achieve your purpose in writing or speaking. If connotations are used correctly, you are able to create an atmosphere in creative writing, an overall emotional impression, a mood.

 Write which level of usage would be most appropriate for the following situations.

1.24 A campaign speech delivered to the student body _____

1.25 A book report written for an English teacher _____

1.26 A speech on disarmament for a regional speech contest _____

1.27 A letter to a vacationing sister _____

1.28 An oral report delivered to the church's young people's group _____

Complete the following lists.

1.29 List three impressions our use of English can give about ourselves.

a. _____

b. _____

c. _____

1.30 List two reasons why Americans have regional dialects.

a. _____

b. _____

Find the words in the sentences that have *negative* connotations.

Write the word after the sentence.

1.31 My brother says that Helen is slender, but I think she's skinny. _____

1.32 Some historians have found the senator to be firm of purpose, but Wilson found him stubborn. _____

1.33 The arrested young man called his vandalism a boyish prank. _____

1.34 Mrs. Eliot has called her outspoken son a radical. _____

Describe the overall mood, atmosphere, or underlying idea of the excerpts and write the words that have connotations that contribute to that mood or idea.

1.35 He was leaning against the ledge of an open lattice, but not looking out: his face was turned to the interior gloom. The fire had smouldered to ashes; the room was filled with the damp, mild air of the cloudy evening; and so still, that not only the murmur of the beck down Gimmerton was distinguishable, but its ripples and its gurgling over the pebbles, or through the large stones which it could not cover. (*Wuthering Heights* by Emily Brontë, Chapter 34)

_____

_____

_____

1.36 Skirting the pool she followed the path towards Rainbarrow, occasionally stumbling over twisted furze-roots, tufts of rushes, or oozing lumps of fleshy fungi, which at this season lay scattered about the heath like the rotten liver and lungs of some colossal animal. The moon and stars were closed up by cloud and rain to the degree of extinction. (*The Return of the Native* by Thomas Hardy, Book Fifth, Chapter 7)

_____

_____

_____

1.37 Never can there come fog too thick, never can there come mud and mire too deep, to assort with the groping and floundering condition which this High Court of Chancery, most pestilent of hoary sinners, holds, this day, in the sight of heaven and earth. (*Bleak House* by Charles Dickens, Chapter 1)

_____

_____

_____

_____

The spelling of noun plurals and suffixes. The spelling of noun plurals can sometimes be difficult for some of the reasons you have already reviewed. The following rules should help you considerably; consult Language Arts 1002, Section 1, if you need examples.

1. Most nouns form their plurals by adding -*s*.
2. Nouns ending in *s, ss, ski, ch, x,* or *z* form their plurals by adding -*es*.
    Exception: the -*ch* ending pronounced as /*k*/ takes only -*s*.
3. Nouns ending in *y*
    a. preceded by a *vowel*, form their plurals by adding -*s*.
    b. preceded by a *consonant*, form their plurals by changing the *y* to *i* and adding -*es*.
    c. if they are *names* ending in *y*, form their plurals by adding -*s* even if the *y* is preceded by a consonant.
4. Nouns ending in *o*
    a. preceded by a *vowel*, form their plurals by adding -*s*.
    b. preceded by a *consonant*, form their plurals
        i.   by adding -*s*, usually, if they are *musical* terms.
        ii. by adding -*s*, sometimes, if the *o* is preceded by a *consonant*.
        iii. by adding -*es*, sometimes, even if the *o* is preceded by a *consonant*;
             check a dictionary.
5. Nouns ending in -*f* or -*fe*
    a. usually form their plurals by adding -*s*.
    b. may possibly form their plurals by changing the *f* or *fe* to *v* and adding -*es* (*knives, loaves, leaves*).
    c. may possibly form their plurals either by adding -*s* or by using the -*ves* ending.
6. Compound nouns
    a. usually form their plurals by adding -*s* or -*es* to the final word in the compound.
    b. may form their plurals by adding -*s* to the main word.
    c. may not fit either rule *a* or *b*; check a dictionary.
7. Nouns ending in the suffix -*ful* form their plurals by adding -*s* to -*ful*.

8. Irregular noun plurals, usually based on Old English forms
   a. may form their plurals by changing their vowel sound (*men, feet, mice*).
   b. may form their plurals by adding an old plural ending (*oxen, children*).
   c. may fit neither rule a nor b if combined with other words to form compounds (*mousetraps, women drivers*); check a dictionary.
9. Foreign plurals
   a. may take *-s* or *-es*.
   b. may keep their foreign plural endings (*bases, crises, alumni*).
   c. may take either an English or a foreign plural; check a dictionary.
10. Some nouns may have one form for both singular and plural (*deer, moose, trout*).
    a. Some nouns with the same form have an s in both the singular and plural (*corps, Swiss*).
    b. Some of the s-ending nouns are used more frequently in either the singular or plural (*news, mathematics* in the singular; *slacks, pants* in plural).
11. Numbers, letters, signs, and words used as words form their plurals by adding *'s* (*if's, k's, 2's*).

 Examine the following sentences carefully.

If you find an error, underline it. Write the correction in the blank following the sentence. Identity the error by the number and letter (if necessary) of the preceding rule that applies to the error. If the sentence is correct, write a C in the blank. If the sentence contains an error, it will contain only one error per sentence.

Example: Dogs and <u>wolfs</u> are in the same family. _____ wolves 5 b _____

1.38 How many active volcanoes are in Hawaii? _____

1.39 Zooes are going to need public support. _____

1.40 Several storys denied that Bam toys are made of poisonous plastic. _____

1.41 Cows and calfs should be sheltered in the winter. _____

1.42 Tariffs are dangerous restraints on trade. _____

1.43 Mules and oxes are useful beasts of burden. _____

1.44 Both my sister-in-laws are good babysitters. _____

1.45 Parenthesises should be placed around less important information. _____

1.46 Teaspoonfuls of lemon juice can enhance the flavor of whitefish. _____

1.47 The uh's in his speech were annoying. _____

Suffixes are added to the ends of words to give them new meaning or functions.

Define the following words using the meanings of the suffixes listed in Section 1 of Language Arts 1002.

1.48 comfortable _____

1.49 applicant _____

1.50 hungry _____

1.51 servitude _____

Spelling suffixes can be confusing. Review the following rules. If you need to see examples, consult Language Arts 1002, Section 1.

1. Words ending in *y*
   a. preceded by a *vowel*, take the suffix without changing the *y*.
   b. preceded by a *consonant*, take the suffix after the *y* has been changed to *i*, unless the suffix begins with *i*.
   c. may not follow rules *a* or *b* (*daily, dryness, shyness*).
2. Words ending in *ie* take the suffix *-ing* after the *ie* has been changed to *y*.
3. Words ending in a silent *e*
   a. preceded by a *consonant*, drop the final *e* if the suffix begins with a vowel.
   b. preceded by a *vowel*, frequently drop the final *e*.
   c. preceded by another *e*, drop only one *e* before adding a suffix beginning with *e* (*-ed, -en*).
   d. retain the final *e* if the suffix begins with a consonant.
   e. retain the final *e* if it is preceded by *c* or *g* and if the suffix begins with *a* or *o*.
4. Words ending in a *consonant*
   a. must have the final consonant doubled if the suffix begins with a vowel, if the word contains only one syllable, and if the final consonant is preceded by a single vowel.
   b. must have the final consonant doubled if the suffix begins with a vowel and if the accent falls on the last syllable of a word with several syllables.
   c. will not have the final consonant doubled if the word contains only one syllable and if the final consonant is preceded by more than one vowel.
   d. will not have the final consonant doubled if the word contains more than one syllable and if the accent does not fall on the last syllable.
   e. will not have the final consonant doubled if the suffix begins with a consonant.
5. Whether you should use an *-able* or *-ible* suffix can sometimes be determined by consulting a word with the same root; if that word is closely related to the word you are spelling, note whether *-able* or *-ible* was used. If a word ending in *-ation*, *-ition*, or *-ion* is not a close comparison, *-able* is probably the correct suffix to use.
6. Whether you should use the *-ize* or *-ise* suffix depends on whether a word is nearly complete before the ending is added. If it is nearly complete, *-ize* is usually correct. If it is not complete or nearly complete, then rise is usually correct.

Read the following sentences.

If you find an error, underline it, write the correction in the blank following the sentence, and identify the error by the number and letter of the rule that applies to the error. If the sentence is correct, write a *C* in the blank. If an error occurs, each sentence will have only one.

1.52 The bird was freed because it would have broken its wings in the cage.

_____

1.53 Always avoid wordyness in writing a descriptive passage. _____

1.54 The speaker's reliance on notes made the question-and-answer session dull.

_____

1.55 The arguements against establishing a student disciplinary committee are unconvincing.

_____

1.56 What experiences and achievements qualify you for this job? _____

1.57 The disease is dangerous but controlable. _____

1.58 The dieing poet asked to be buried in the country he had described in his poems.

_____

1.59 Jesus extended His blessings to those men and women who needed His forgiveness most;

when He first met them, they were not always humble or virtueous. _____

1.60 Recent studies emphasise that smoking is destructive for every age group.

_____

1.61 Choose words with preciseion and care. _____

Suffixes are useful for increasing our reading, writing, and speaking vocabularies. As you speak and write, suffixes help you to use familiar words in several positions requiring different parts of speech. As you read, suffixes help you to understand difficult words. The following list should help you to review the changes that suffixes can make. Examples are in Language Arts 1002, Section 1.

Suffixes can change
1. verbs to nouns (-*ment*).
2. adjectives to nouns (-*dom*, -*ness*).
3. nouns to verbs (-*ise* -*ize*, -*fy*).
4. nouns to adjectives (-*ish*, -*ly*).
5. adjectives to adverbs (-*ly*).
6. adjectives to other parts of speech (-*en*, -*ize*).

 For the word in parenthesis, write the correct form (a), list the part of speech (b), list the part of speech to which you will have to convert the word so that the sentence makes sense (c), and write the number from the preceding list of the change taking place (d).

1.62 Roses usually a. _____ empty corners. (beauty)

   b. _____ c. _____ d. _____

1.63 Writing a ten-page report is a time-consuming a. _____ . (assign)

   b. _____ c. _____ d. _____

1.64 Admitting his mistake was a(n) a. _____ act. (man)

   b. _____ c. _____ d. _____

1.65 Jesus's followers a. _____ gave their belongings to the poor. (happy)

   b. _____ c. _____ d. _____

1.66 The dark clouds will a. _____ as the sun goes down. (light)

   b. _____ c. _____ d. _____

1.67 The man showed great a. _____ in his decision. (wise)

   b. _____ c. _____ d. _____

UNDERSTANDING AND CONSTRUCTING SENTENCES

You remember that a *sentence* must have a subject and a predicate, and that it must express a complete thought. Now that you have reviewed how words have developed and how they are formed, you are ready to review how they function or work together to form sentences.

Verbals. Verbals are verb forms that function as nouns or modifiers while retaining the characteristics of verbs. They are useful in writing because they enable the writer to combine thoughts without using unnecessary words and because their structure provides a variety that would not be possible by simply writing all thoughts in clauses. The three types of verbals are listed, defined, and explained here. Consult Language Arts 1003, Section 2, for further information.

1. *Participles* are verbals used as adjectives. present participle ending, *-ing* (*praying*) past participle ending, usually *-ed* (*prayed*); irregular verbs vary (*written*)

2. *Infinitives* are verbals preceded by *to* and used as nouns, adjectives, or adverbs. (*to forgive, to be forgiven*)

3. *Gerunds* are verbals ending in *-ing* and used as nouns.

 Use verbals to combine the following groups into one sentence.

1.68 He ran swiftly. He was able to overtake the child.

_____

1.69 I know that I can do better. This knowledge will help me to persist.

_____

Underline the verbals in the following sentences and write after each sentence whether the verbals underlined are participles, gerunds, or infinitives, and how they function (as subject, object, predicate nominative, adverb, adjective).

1.70 I recall participating in a spelling bee.

a. _____   b. _____

1.71 There's always plenty of work to be done in any small town.

a. _____   b. _____

1.72 His greatest ambition is to follow in his father's footsteps.

a. _____   b. _____

1.73 We must not shrink from exploring our mistakes as well as our successes.

a. _____   b. _____

1.74 Wounded and starving, the wolf left the pack to die.

a. _____   b. _____

Phrases. A phrase is a group of related words lacking a subject and a predicate and functioning as a single grammatical unit. The following types were presented in Language Arts 1003, Section 2:

1. *Prepositional phrases* begin with such words (prepositions) as these:

of	by	over	above	before	into
in	for	on	after	behind	inside
to	from	with	against	below	under
at	in	about	among	except	upon

Prepositions take objects (which may have modifiers), and the prepositional phrases may function as adjectives, adverbs, or nouns.

2. *Participial phrases* are composed of participles and their objects and modifiers. The phrases function as adjectives and should be placed as close as possible to the words modified. A "dangling" modifier may result if the participial phrase is placed at the beginning of a sentence but does not modify the subject that follows.

3. *Gerund phrases* are composed of gerunds and their objects and modifiers. They function as nouns.

4. *Infinitive phrases* are composed of infinitives and their objects and modifiers. They may function as nouns, adjectives, or adverbs.

Underline the phrases in the following sentences and write the functions of those phrases on the lines.

1.75 Mary found Jesus questioning the priests. _____

1.76 Choose your words with great care. _____

1.77 Earning money has been a difficult task this summer. _____

1.78 Why do you want to destroy this animal's burrow? _____

1.79 Her main concern was wearing a diamond necklace. _____

1.80 The best topic to write about is one you know well. _____

1.81 Many scientists have been researching the possibility of black holes. _____

Write sentences.

1.82 Use a prepositional phrase as an adjective. _____

_____

1.83 Use a prepositional phrase as an adverb. _____

_____

1.84 Use a participial phrase. _____

_____

1.85 Use a gerund phrase as a subject. _____

_____

1.86 Use a gerund phrase as an object. _____

_____

1.87 Use an infinitive phrase as an object. _____

_____

Subordinate clauses (also called dependent clauses). Subordinate clauses subordinate less important ideas to more important ones. Although subordinate clauses do have subjects and predicates, they are not complete sentences by themselves. Review the following types found in Language Arts 1006, Section 1:

1. *Adjective clauses* modify nouns or pronouns. *Relative pronouns* (*who, whom, whose* referring to people; *which* referring to things, animals, or groups; and *that* referring to people and things) introduce adjective clauses,

    OR *subordinate conjunctions*, sometimes called relative adverbs—such as *where, when, why*—introduce adjective clauses,

    OR the *understood conjunction* or *pronoun* may be absent.

Restrictive adjective clauses are necessary to the meaning of the nouns or pronouns modified and are not set off with commas.

Nonrestrictive adjective clauses are unnecessary and should be set off by commas. In the sentence, "The man who is entering that room should be stopped," we do not use commas because we need to know which man should be stopped. In the sentence, "John Sistine, who is president of the Painter's Club, will speak tomorrow," we use commas because the specific name *John Sistine* has already identified the man without the added clause.

2. *Adverb clauses* modify verbs, adjectives, or adverbs. *Subordinate conjunctions* introduce adverb clauses:

When?	while, when, whenever, as, as soon as, before, after, since, until
Where?	where, wherever
How?	as if, as though
Why?	because, since, as, so that, for, in case
On what condition?	if, unless, though, although, even though, provided that, whether
Comparison/Contrast	than, as

3. *Noun clauses* function as subjects, objects, complements, predicate nominatives, or in any way that a noun can function. Relative pronouns or subordinate conjunctions may introduce them.

Combine these ideas into one sentence using subordinate clauses.

1.88 John Keats wrote poetry about art's relationship with life.
Keats lived in the nineteenth century.

_____

_____

_____

1.89 You should prepare to go on stage at the right time. I shall tell you the best time.

_____

_____

_____

1.90 Instead of preaching about punishment and revenge, Jesus taught two things.
We should love and forgive each other, He taught

_____

_____

_____

1.91 Betty sent some beautiful flowers. I put them in my brightest window.

_____

_____

_____

Write sentences with clauses performing the following functions.

1.92 predicate nominative _____

_____

1.93 modifier to the subject _____

_____

1.94 modifier to the verb _____

_____

Pronouns. Pronouns are substituted for nouns. They should have one-word **antecedents**. The following explains the six categories of pronouns discussed in Language Arts 1006, Section 2:

1. *Relative pronouns (who, whom, whose, which, and that)* introduce dependent clauses.

2. *Interrogative pronouns (who, whom, whose, which, what)* ask questions.

3. *Demonstrative pronouns (this, that, these, those)* point out to whom or to what the speaker is referring.

4. *Indefinite pronouns* do not specify definite or specific things:

    Always singular.   one, anyone, someone, no one, everyone, anybody, somebody, nobody, everybody, anything, something, nothing, everything, either, neither, another, each

    Always plural: both, few, many, others, several

    Either singular or plural (depending on whether it refers to a singular or plural noun):   some, all, most, none, any

5. *Compound-personal pronouns* end with the words *self* or *selves* and may be either **reflexive** or **intensive**. Do not use a "self" pronoun unless the antecedent has already appeared in the sentence. Language Arts 1006, has specific examples.

6. *Personal pronouns* designate the person speaking, spoken to, or spoken about. They may have masculine, feminine, or neuter *gender*. The following chart should help you to review the cases of personal pronouns:

SINGULAR		
Nominative case (subject, predicate nominative)	Objective case (direct object, indirect object, object of preposition)	Possessive case
1st person	I	me	my [mine]
2nd person	you	you	your, [yours]*
3rd person	he, she, it	him, her, it	his, her, its*, [hers]*
PLURAL		
1st person	we	us	our [ours]*
2nd person	you	you	your [yours]*
3rd person	they	them	their [theirs]*

[ ]'s indicate noun substitutes.

 * indicates that *no* apostrophe is used.

Reminders to prevent problems:

1. Be alert to *elliptical* clauses (clauses with words left out); supply the missing words mentally so that you can discover the use and case of any pronoun that confuses you.

2. Remember that *whom* is in the objective case; never use it as a subject or predicate nominative.

3. Use the pronoun *it*, instead of they, as a pronoun for collective nouns used as a unit.

4. Make certain that pronouns agree with their antecedents in *person*, *number* (singular or plural), and *gender*.

5. Make certain that each pronoun has a clear, one-word antecedent.

6. Place pronouns as close as possible to their antecedents to avoid confusion.

7. If the gender of the individual is unknown or unspecified, the pronoun 'they' can be used as a singular pronoun.

8. When referring to multiple people or hypothetical people, use the word 'they' to avoid any inaccurate gender identifications.

Write the appropriate pronoun form on the line.

1.95 (Who, Whom) _____ should we select as our temporary chairman?

1.96 Give the letters to Jean and (I, me) _____ .

1.97 Charles is more eager to have the job than (I, me) _____ .

1.98 Would you like Fred and (myself, me) _____ to leave for lunch now?

1.99 Some people are able to laugh at (themselves, they, them) _____ .

1.100 The woodpeckers (that, who) _____ nest in this tree wake us up.

1.101 I (myself, me) _____ was moved by the sermon.

1.102 Sara intends to rehearse her speech by reading it to Ellen and (myself, I, me).

_____

1.103 _____ could never accept (its, it's) _____ conclusion.

Explain why the following sentences are unclear.

1.104 Julie went with Sarah to the supper. She was happy.

_____

1.105 Yesterday we cleaned the yard, which took longer than we had planned.

_____

1.106 I heard Mom and Dad scolding Mac for his drop in grades. That has been going on for a long time.

_____

Sentences. Sentences have both subjects and predicates and express complete, independent thoughts. They work together to develop paragraphs, which are the basic building units of a composition. Reviewing the following sentence types should enable you to add variety and logic to your writing.

1. *A simple sentence* has at least one subject and one predicate (the subject and predicate may be compound, however).

2. *A compound sentence* contains at least two complete thoughts or independent phrases and can be divided into two or more simple sentences. These independent clauses are usually joined by a **coordinating conjunction** (*and, but, or*), or sometimes by a *semicolon* (;). These thoughts are usually joined because they are *closely related in meaning*.

3. *A complex sentence* contains one complete (or independent) clause and one or more sub-ordinate (or dependent) clauses. You have already reviewed the ways that subordinate clauses are introduced. Complex sentences connect ideas and indicate their relative importance by subordinating less important thoughts to more important ones.

4. *A compound-complex sentence* contains two or more independent clauses and one or more subordinate clauses.

Write *S* for simple, *C* for compound, *Cx* for complex, *CC* for compound-complex, or *F* for fragment.

1.107 _____ If that was the design, it certainly succeeded.

1.108 _____ I told him a friend of mine had commissioned me to make some inquiries about a cherished companion.

1.109 _____ He never smiled, he never frowned, he never changed his voice from the gentle-flowing key to which he turned the initial sentence.

1.110 _____ She was one of those charming girls, born by a freak of destiny in a family of toilers.

1.111 _____ She dressed simply, because she had no means of adornment.

1.112 _____ When he and himself agreed upon anything.

1.113 _____ And yet, that awful tiger, those shrieks, that blood!

Rewrite the following passage; combine thoughts to produce compound sentences and show logical relationships by subordinating less important clauses to more important ones. Use proper conjunctions, and use verbals or phrases wherever needed.

1.114   The sky was growing gray. The clouds were darkening. The sun was low. It was tinged with red. A biting wind blew. It was from the north. The tree branches whispered. The birds did not sing. They had gone to sleep. I was lonely. I thought about a warm walk last spring.

_____

_____

_____

_____

_____

_____

ORGANIZING PARAGRAPHS

A paragraph may have any number of sentences, but must develop one main idea. It can be thought of as a composition in miniature. It is usually developed in much the same way as a composition: by examples, comparisons and contrasts, explanations (or definitions), or arguments (or reasons) making the meaning of the topic sentence clear.

Follow these steps to construct a paragraph:

1.   Write a _topic sentence_ that states the subject of the paragraph.

2.   Develop the topic sentence by using sentences that give examples, comparisons, explanations, or arguments.

3.   Organize these supporting sentences carefully by importance, steps, time, or space (order with which objects are observed).

4.   Avoid introducing sentences that do not support the topic sentence, and avoid repeating ideas.

5.   End the paragraph by summarizing or referring to the topic sentence.

6.   Begin a new paragraph when you want to make a change of focus in one of the following areas (see Language Arts 1005, Section 1):

time	point of view	place	speaker
action	idea	mood	step

7.   Use **connectives** and _transitions_ to join paragraphs and sentences.

   a.   Repeat _key words_ or _patterns_ from previous sentences or paragraphs (called "Echo" in Language Arts 1005).

   b.   Refer to the topic being discussed with such words as _this, that, these, such, those_.

c. Use *pronouns* with antecedents in previous sentences or paragraphs.

d. Use *conjunctions* or *adverbs* with appropriate meanings
(a larger list is in Section 1 of Language Arts 1005):

i. *To add ideas*—and, more, also, too, besides, similarly, in the same way

ii. *To take away, limit,* or *oppose*—but, however, nevertheless, yet, though, on the other hand

iii. *To show time*—while then, meanwhile, later, soon, now

iv. *To show order*—next, finally, then, first, second

v. *To introduce an example*—for example, for instance, to illustrate

vi. *To show a result or conclusion*—therefore, for this reason, as a result, consequently

vii. *To repeat an idea*—in other words, in summary, in short, briefly

viii. *To compare*—likewise, similarly, in the same way

ix. *To show space*—beneath, straight ahead, on the left, in the middle, to the right

e. Be sure the contents of the sentences or paragraphs are related; no repetition, connectives or transitions can tie together unrelated ideas logically.

 Make paragraph divisions in the following passages. Underline the beginning of the sentence that should begin a new paragraph, and explain the change of focus in the blank; is it *time, place, action, mood, point of view, speaker, idea,* or *step*?

1.115 The only hope for the youth in which there was any element of certainty was based upon the success of the princess in discovering this mystery; and the moment he looked upon her, he saw she had succeeded, as in his soul he knew she would succeed. Then it was that his quick and anxious glance asked the question: "Which?" It was as plain to her as if he shouted it from where he stood. There was not an instant to be lost. (from "The Lady, or the Tiger," by Frank R. Stockton).

_____

1.116 Then he says, "One–two–three–jump!" and him and the feller touched up the frogs from behind, and the frog hopped off, but Dan'l give a heave, and hysted up his shoulders—so—like a Frenchman, but it wan't no use—he couldn't budge; he was planted as solid as an anvil, and he couldn't no more stir than if he was anchored out. Smiley was a good deal surprised, and he was disgusted too, but he didn't have no idea what the matter was, of course. The feller took the money and started away; and when he was going out at the door, he sorter jerked his thumb over his shoulders—this way—at Dan'l and says again, very deliberate, "Well, I don't see no p'ints about that frog that's any better'n any other frog." (from "The Celebrated Jumping Frog of Calaveras County," by Mark Twain).

_____

Write a paragraph.

1.117 Answer the following questions and write the completed paragraph in the space that follows or on a separate sheet of paper. Pay close attention to spelling, word formation, phrases, clauses, and sentence variety and arrangement.

a. What is the topic you have selected?

_____

b. What method will you use to support or explain your topic?

_____

c. Write your paragraph, arranging your support carefully.

_____

_____

_____

TEACHER CHECK _____ _____
                        initials   date

PUNCTUATING IDEAS

A skilled writer's punctuation is rarely noticeable, but an unskilled writer's punctuation can become so obvious that it annoys and misleads readers. Properly placed punctuation marks should enable readers to group together and separate ideas naturally and meaningfully. Remember that readers cannot hear your voice pause or fall; they must rely on your punctuation. Review the following basic rules. Make certain that your review of sentence types and conjunctions has been thorough. Punctuation examples may be found in Language Arts 1008, Section 3.

Commas

1. Place a comma before a conjunction introducing an independent clause.
2. Set off a *nonrestrictive* dependent clause with commas. Note that *restrictive* dependent clauses are not set off by commas.
3. Set off **appositives** (nouns, pronouns, or noun or pronoun phrases that follow another noun or pronoun to explain it, and are grammatically the same) with commas.
4. When using quotation marks, place a comma or period *within* the quotation marks.
5. Set off words of *direct address* (names of those spoken to directly) with commas.

Semicolons

1. Join two independent clauses with a semicolon if a conjunction is not used.
2. Use both a semicolon and a conjunction to join two independent clauses *if* one of the independent clauses contains commas.
3. Place semicolons (if needed) outside quotation marks.

Quotation Marks

1. Put quotation marks around only the words a character actually speaks. Remember that introducing a new speaker requires a new paragraph.

2. Place commas or periods inside final quotation marks, and colons or semicolons outside the final marks. Question marks or exclamation points are placed inside quotation marks if they punctuate *only* the quotation. If they punctuate the entire sentence (including words outside the quotation), they are placed outside the quotation marks.

3. Do not place punctuation marks around an *indirect* quotation, a summary of what was said.

Apostrophes

1. Add -'s to form the possessive of words that do not end in *s*.

2. Add -'s to form the possessive of words with *singular* forms ending in *s*.

3. Add only an apostrophe (') to form the possessive of words with *plural* forms ending in *s*.

4. Add the possessive ending only to the second noun to show joint ownership.

5. Add the possessive ending to both nouns to show separate ownership.

6. Add the possessive ending to only the *last* word of compounds.

7. Note that possessive personal pronoun forms do *not* require apostrophes.

8. Use an apostrophe to form a *contraction* (a combination of words in which letters have been dropped).

9. Do not confuse the contractions *you're*, *it's*, and *they're* with the personal pronouns *your*, *its*, and *their*.

 Correct the following sentences by slashing through incorrect punctuation marks, by writing the corrected form above the mistake, and by inserting marks where they are needed.

1.118 John are you certain you understand?" Emily asked.

1.119 Its going to be a long wait the nurse confided.

1.120 Is that notebook your's or mine?

1.121 We could wait or we could leave.

1.122 Losing the necklace produced a mixed result, she became old with work, but she also became more tolerant of poverty.

1.123 John and Mary house has a large front yard.

1.124 Charles essay was too long and mine was too short.

1.125 We enjoyed the sermon, we found help and comfort for so many of our problems.

1.126 John warned, "I would wait Ellen if I were you."

WRITING COMPOSITIONS

The material that you have reviewed so far has been preparing you for the difficult but exciting process of writing a composition. Even writers whose work has been judged excellent have admitted that writing is not easy and that its difficulty often makes it unpleasant. Yet their skills and practice have enabled them to use their talents wisely, even as those wise servants multiplied their talents in Jesus's story (Matthew 25:14-30).

Your first concern in writing a composition is your reader. You write ideas down so that they may be recorded and read; if you did not want them read, you probably would not bother to put them on paper. Since you want your writing to be read and understood, you need to follow several guidelines to put your meaning into a form that makes sense to someone else. If your writing is hurried and disorganized, your reader will not be able to follow your thinking, and your composition will have been a waste of everyone's time.

Expository writing. You will review the *types* of **expository writing** because most of your future writing will fit into this category. In Language Arts 1006, Section 3, you learned that a writer may use one of, or a combination of, six types of expository structure:

1. cause and effect,
2. definition,
3. classification or division,
4. **process analysis**,
5. comparison or contrast, and
6. illustration or example.

A few of these types should be quite familiar; you have already learned that paragraphs may be developed in some of these ways. Just as you develop and support a topic or main idea in a paragraph, you explain, support, or develop a main idea in an expository composition.

Recipes, instruction sheets, and "how to" articles are all examples of process analysis essays. These essays give excellent practice in making information clear and in ordering it carefully. In writing a process essay, keep the following points in mind:

1. Give instructions clearly without presenting unnecessary opinions or misleading details.

2. Pretend that your instructions are being written for someone who knows nothing about the process being described.

3. Organize the steps carefully according to the order your reader will have to use (probably chronological order).

4. Explain *why* certain steps are necessary.

5. Explain exactly *how* each step is to be done, using examples and comparisons whenever necessary.

If you have an *idea* instead of a process to explain, you can use a number of ways to support or develop that idea. You can *define* the idea, give *examples* of it, *compare* or *contrast* it with something else, or *divide* it into its parts. The **illustrative** paper is a good exercise because writing it teaches you to state your idea or thesis in one sentence in your first paragraph, and then to support that sentence with a number of carefully chosen and described illustrations or examples. Sometimes these examples can be described by comparing them to things that might be more familiar. Often, several types of exposition are mixed together; even though the structure of the composition fits one type, individual paragraphs can be developed using other types.

Label the following topics according to the types of exposition that would provide the best overall structure for the topics. Write *P* for process, *I* for illustrative, *C* for comparison/contrast, *D* for definition, and *CD* for classification/division.

1.127 _____ The meaning of freedom

1.128 _____ Tying a shoe

1.129 _____ Charity should begin at home.

1.130 _____ The structure of Congress

1.131 _____ Grade averages are higher now than they were ten years ago.

Literary critique. Writing a literary critique can involve using a number of the structures previously listed, but it usually requires classifying (discussing by classes) the work of literature and evaluating the skill with which individual elements have been handled. Since readers of your literary critique may rely on your opinions, you should know what you are writing about. You will need to have a solid understanding of the effective use of literary techniques. More importantly, you will need to understand and appreciate the work of literature you are evaluating; you should have read it several times so that your judgment is sound.

The following steps will help you to review the process for writing a literary critique:

1. Read the literary work you intend to "review" several times and write notes about some of its important points, its strengths, and its weaknesses.
2. Read about the author of the literary work and about the setting of the story. If parts of the literary work still confuse you, try to find what some critics have said about the work.
3. Arrange those notes until you have an orderly *outline* to guide you in your writing.
4. Make certain that your outline includes these elements:
   a. brief statements in your introduction about
      i. the time and place of the story (or novel or poem),
      ii. the characters of the story, and
      iii. the plot of the story;
   b. your evaluation of the author's use of *setting, characters, plot, point of view, theme* or *purpose, conflict*, and any other elements that should be mentioned.
5. Allow your outline to sit overnight. Then reread it, making certain that all the points included are important and properly arranged.
6. Ask yourself these questions so that your judgment is thoughtful and fair:
   a. about *setting*:
      i. If the setting is important in the story, are descriptive passages realistic, smoothly written, quotable?
      ii. Does the setting have a mood or atmosphere that contributes to the theme?
      iii. Does the author's description of the setting appeal to your five senses?
   b. about *characters*:
      i. Do the characters behave as people in their situations would behave?

    ii.   Are they interesting? How much do we learn about them?

    iii.   Are their conflicts internal or external?

    iv.   Do they think or do they just act?

    v.   Do the characters learn something about themselves? Do they grow emotionally?

    vi.   Does the plot help us to understand them better?

    vii. Is the dialogue (speech) of the characters realistic and meaningful?

  c.   about *plot*:

    i.   Is all the action necessary?

    ii.   Does the action make sense? Could the plot happen?

    iii.   Is the climax emotional enough to attract our interest?

  d.   about *theme* or *purpose*:

    i.   Does this story (or novel or poem) have a purpose or theme?

    ii.   Is that theme or purpose important enough for us to consider it?

  e.   about *point of view*:

    i.   Are we aware of the person telling the story?

    ii.   Is the person telling the story reliable? Can we believe what they say?

    iii.   Would the story be different (improved or weakened) if it were told by someone else?

7.   Give good reasons for your opinions so that your reader will know whether or not to trust you; give examples from the story.

8.   Write your critique intelligently. Your reader will not value your judgment if there are mistakes in spelling, usage, or organization. Organize paragraphs carefully and vary sentence patterns to make your writing interesting.

Complete the following activity.

1.132 Choose one chapter from the novel you studied in Language Arts 1009, making certain that it is an important chapter for one reason or another. Reread it carefully, take notes on it, and arrange an outline using the instructions given. Write a 500-word paper, giving your judgment of the writing as well as a summary of the plot and a description of the characters. After your paper is written, allow someone in your class to give opinions and to "grade" your use of words, sentences, and paragraphs. Rewrite your paper, if necessary. Then, hand it in to your teacher. Save your outline and critique.

TEACHER CHECK _____ _____
                                            initials   date

Review the material in this section in preparation for the Self Test. The Self Test will check your mastery of this particular section. The items missed on this Self Test will indicate specific areas where restudy is needed for mastery.

SELF TEST 1

Match these items (each answer, 2 points).

1.01 _____ suggestive meaning or atmosphere of a word

1.02 _____ formal, general, or informal

1.03 _____ verbals used only as adjectives

1.04 _____ clauses unnecessary to the meaning of the words modified; they are set off by commas

1.05 _____ the history of a word

1.06 _____ clauses necessary to the meaning of the words modified; they are *not* set off by commas

1.07 _____ word endings indicating grammatical function

1.08 _____ verbals preceded by to and used as nouns, adjectives, and adverbs

1.09 _____ a definition no longer in use

1.010 _____ fixed word order

a. syntax

b. obsolete

c. infinitives

d. participles

e. etymology

f. restrictive

g. connotation

h. levels of usage

i. denotation

j. nonrestrictive

k. inflections

Write the letter of the correct answer on each line (each answer, 2 points).

1.011 Verbals ending in -*ing* and used only as nouns are _____ .
a. participles   b. gerunds   c. infinitives   d. inflections

1.012 Words for which pronouns stand are _____ .
a. antecedents   b. connotations   c. inflections   d. infinitives

1.013 A pronoun ending in -*self* and referring to the previously used noun or pronoun is _____ .
a. complex   b. reflexive   c. obtuse   d. restrictive

1.014 A pronoun ending in -*self* and emphasizing the previously used noun or pronoun by immediate repetition is _____ .
a. complex   b. reflexive   c. intensive   d. compound

1.015 A sentence that contains at least two independent clauses is a _____ .
a. simple sentence   b. compound sentence
c. complex sentence   d. fragment

1.016 A sentence that contains one independent clause and one or more dependent clauses is a _____ .
a. simple sentence   b. compound sentence
c. complex sentence   d. fragment

1.017 Recipes, instruction sheets, and "How to" articles are types of _____ .
a. illustrative texts
b. literary texts
c. comparison texts
d. process analysis

1.018 A sentence that has at least one subject and one predicate and that expresses a complete thought is a _____ .
a simple sentence
b. dependent clause
c. fragment
d. prepositional phrase

1.019 Nouns, pronouns, or phrases that follow another noun or pronoun to explain it and are grammatically the same are _____ .
a. antecedents
b. gerunds
c. inflections
d. appositives

1.020 An essay that has a thesis supported with examples is _____ .
a. a process analysis essay
b. an illustrative essay
c. an instruction sheet
d. a classification essay

Correct these sentences by underlining the error and writing the correction in the blank following each sentence (each numbered item, 3 points).

1.021 Characters in short storys are revealed through their actions.

_____

1.022 Always avoid wordyness in writing a descriptive passage.

_____

1.023 Choose words with precision and care.

_____

1.024 The dark clouds will light as the sun lowers.

_____

1.025 Charles Dickens was unable, to finish his last novel.

_____

1.026 Instead of preaching about punishment and revenge.

_____

1.027 The man, who is entering that room, should be stopped.

_____

1.028 Finishing the final paragraph, the introduction did not fit.

_____

1.029 Someone from our school always go to the district speech contest.

_____

1.030 Who did Ellen give that job?

_____

1.031 Those poems and these short story should make an enjoyable reading collection.

_____

1.032 It's a lovely book; I didn't know that it is your's

_____

1.033 Julie went with Sarah to the supper. She was happy.

_____

1.034 Losing the necklace produced a mixed result, she became old with work, but she also became tolerant of poverty.

_____

1.035 John warned, "I would wait Ellen if I were you."

_____

Complete these exercises (each answer, 5 points).

1.036 Explain what is improper in the following character's speech:
Miss Eliot looked up from her desk. "Elizabeth, you are a precocious young woman; I find your most recent composition utterly super."

_____

1.037 Explain the reason that the word _flow_ probably does not fit in the following description:
The sun seared the bread crust that dropped from her parched lips. She raised her cracked hands and pushed her flowing sleeves up her arms.

_____

1.038 Subordinate less important ideas in the following sentence:
Charles was tired of listening to the concert and it was dark enough that his father could not see him so he slipped out into the lobby.

_____

| 80 |
| 100 |

SCORE _____   TEACHER _____ _____
                                                           initials   date

2. SPEAKING

When members of classes, church groups, social and civic clubs, and professional organizations gather together, they gain strength and a sense of unity from contributing to those groups. A carefully researched and organized speech, effectively delivered, can be a worthwhile contribution to any group. Yet many members of groups would rather listen than share their knowledge and ideas; they claim that they simply are not good speakers.

They fail to realize that most "good speakers" have *learned* how to speak well and have *practiced* to perfect their skills. Effective speaking can be compared to effective writing; both require skill, practice, and much hard work. More importantly, both means of communication are responsibilities that thinking and sensitive people should accept.

Section Objectives

Review the following objectives. When you have completed this section, you should be able to:

6. Explain the elements of a speech.
7. Identify the elements of oral interpretation.
8. Explain necessary listening skills.

Vocabulary

Study the following words to enhance your learning success in this section.

chronological sequence	clichés	optimum pitch
pitch	resonance	

DESCRIBING FEELINGS AND THOUGHTS

In Section 1 you were told to keep your reader in mind during the entire writing process. You were reminded to use appropriate words; to structure sentences with clarity, variety, and conciseness; and to organize those sentences coherently into logical, concise paragraphs. You were told to emphasize major points by organizing compositions according to recognized patterns of development. As you speak, your hearer becomes a responsive audience. If your ideas are not emphasized, or if your organization or usage offends your listeners, they may look puzzled, annoyed, bored, or entirely disinterested. All that you have learned about writing becomes doubly important as you speak.

Selecting and limiting a topic. Selecting and limiting a topic for a speech is a time-consuming but essential step unless your topic has been assigned to you. If you will be selecting your own topic, remember to:

1. *think* about issues that are important to you,

2. *listen* to yourself as you discuss those issues,

3. *sort* out overly emotional and poorly developed topics, and

4. *choose* a topic about which you are informed.

After your topic is selected, limit it. Jot down everything you know about the topic; then:

1. *look carefully for related points* in the ideas you have jotted down,

2. *eliminate unrelated ideas*, and

3. *choose an interesting focus or approach* that can be discussed and supported in the amount of time allowed for your speech.

Outlining the topic. Outlining a topic begins when you arrange those related points into some sort of order. If you intend to retell, or narrate, an event, you will probably arrange your outline in a **chronological sequence**. If your speech will have an expository structure, you need to consider the six types of exposition you just reviewed in Section 1. Remember to choose examples or arguments that will appeal to your audience's predominant age and professional interests. A ladies' reading club probably will not be interested in auto racing, for example. Arrange your outline, using Roman numerals for main points and capital letters for the details and examples amplifying each main point.

Answer *true* or *false*.

2.1 _____ You should choose a topic on which you know nothing so that you can educate yourself as you prepare your speech.

2.2 _____ You should sort out topics that could not be developed.

2.3 _____ You should sort out topics about which you are overly emotional.

2.4 _____ You can limit your topic by looking carefully for related points in the ideas you have jotted down, by eliminating unrelated ideas, and by choosing an interesting focus or approach.

2.5 _____ Choose a topic and examples that would not interest your audience so that you can broaden their experience.

2.6 _____ In your outline use Roman numerals for main points.

Complete the following activity.

2.7 Take out the outline you used for your literary critique written at the end of Section 1.
Do you think you spent enough time arranging and rearranging it?
If you heard those main points in someone else's speech, could you follow them?

Write your own evaluation of your outline.

_____

_____

_____

_____

_____

_____

_____

_____

_____

_____

_____

_____

TEACHER CHECK _____ _____
                                      initials   date

Choosing the language. The language for a speech requires careful thought. The following guidelines should help to make your speech interesting and clear (details are in Language Arts 1002, Section 2):

1. Adjectives should be descriptive, necessary, appropriate, and specific.

2. Difficult words should be defined or avoided.

3. **Clichés** should be eliminated.

4. Words should have connotations that will be favorable to the audience.

5. The overall level of usage should be neither too formal nor too casual for your audience.

6. Check for grammar errors, such as double negatives (two negative words within the same construction—He couldn't hardly get to work), incorrect verb forms, incorrect pronoun forms, or needless repetitions, must be avoided since you want your audience to respect your judgment.

 Read the following paragraphs from a speech written for a group of high school English students. Underline any language that is inappropriate and write corrections and the numbers of the guidelines that apply on the lines which follow.

Many high school English programs are not very good at getting students ready for college. My brother took easy courses at his high school, like flicks courses, sci-fi courses, you know. Well, he flunked out of English at college. My sister thought she was taking real hard courses at her high school, but she fell flat as a pancake at State U.

2.8 _____

2.9 _____

2.10 _____

2.11 _____

2.12 _____

2.13 _____

2.14 _____

2.15 _____

2.16 _____

Writing the speech. Writing a speech should be a careful process. Make certain that the major points of your speech are emphasized so that your listeners will be able to follow your ideas. Often, speech writers outline those points in their introduction and summarize them in their conclusion. After writing your speech but before you begin to rehearse it, you must revise it carefully using the following points (from Language Arts 1002, Section 2):

1. Reread your paper.
   Change vague words into specific ones.
   Correct any grammatical errors.
   Omit meaningless fillers.
   Correct usage errors.

2. Check the tone of your paper.
   Change any parts that are too formal.
   Change any parts that are too informal.
   Correct any conversational or slang expressions.
   Be sure that your tone (your attitude toward your speech) is suitable for your speech's purpose and your audience.

3. Consider the audience.
   Change any parts that are too difficult or confusing.
   Change any parts that are too simple. Do not insult your audience's intelligence.
   Try to make any dull parts more interesting.
   Make certain that your speech is suitable for your audience.

4. Refine the descriptive language.
   Make certain that each passage is accurate.
   Make certain that each passage is expressed in the clearest, most descriptive language possible.

5. Test your speech.
   Read it aloud or make a recording of it.
   Make certain your words and ideas flow smoothly.
   Read your speech to someone else for criticism.

 Write the letter of the correct answer on each line.

2.17 To make certain that the major points of your speech are clear, _____ .
   a. mention them in your conclusion
   b. emphasize them as they occur in your speech
   c. list them in your introduction
   d. list them in the introduction, emphasize them as they occur, and mention them in the conclusion

2.18 To improve the tone of your paper, _____ .

    a. make the language formal to impress your audience with your knowledge

    b. make the language conversational to seem friendly

    c. make the language suitable for the audience, avoiding language that is too formal or conversational

    d. make the language dull so that the focus will be on ideas

2.19 A poor way to test a speech is to _____ .

    a. read it aloud to someone else for criticism

    b. make a recording of it

    c. lay it aside so that you will not be tired of it

    d. read it to yourself, listening to the words and connections between ideas

Complete the following activity.

2.20 Evaluate your literary critique written at the end of Section 1 using the points previously listed. Would your teacher's evaluation of your composition have been higher if you had revised your paper carefully? Why? How?

_____

_____

_____

_____

_____

_____

_____

_____

_____

_____

_____

_____

_____

_____

TEACHER CHECK _____ _____

                                               initials   date

Delivering the speech. Speaking effectively requires practice. Speaking is also more effective if you are aware of techniques that can make your voice more pleasant and your gestures more relaxed (see Language Arts 1007, Section 1 for details).

To improve your voice's *volume*, take deep breaths, breathing from your diaphragm. Breaths supported with lower muscles will last longer. They enable you to relax so that you can phrase words properly.

To improve your voice's **resonance**, practice these exercises: tighten and relax your jaws, yawn, take quick gasps, and exercise your shoulder and neck muscles. Note that these activities are exercises, not practices to use while speaking. To use **pitch** effectively, find your **optimum pitch** and learn how you may vary pitch for different purposes. You may intimate fine distinctions of meaning by sliding your pitch while saying certain words. You may emphasize passages by varying pitch between words. Finally, you may give a speech or oral reading a specific mood or atmosphere by using the appropriate pitch (by using a thin, excited voice to indicate excitement, for example).

To improve *enunciation*, make certain that you know the proper pronunciation of difficult words, practice frequently so that difficult words are spoken easily, and speak slowly enough that every syllable can be heard.

To exhibit effective body language and posture, stand straight but relaxed. If you feel your body growing tense during a speech, take a few steps at a transition in your speech. To further share your feelings and thoughts, use suitable, natural facial expressions and gestures, practicing them in front of a mirror.

To establish contact with your audience, try to look directly at individual members of the audience. If direct eye contact makes you nervous, look slightly over their heads. Do not stare at one spot that is removed from the audience.

To improve your presentation if your speech is not memorized, type it on loose pages so that you can move them quietly. Mark your speech with signals that remind you of the phrasing and emphasis on which you have decided (standard markings: / indicates a short pause, // indicates a longer pause, (word) indicates that the underlined word is stressed with the voice).

To locate speaking problems, try to make an electronic recording of your speech with a phone or computer.

Complete the following sentences.

2.21 Take deep breaths supported with lower muscles to enable yourself to relax and

_____ .

2.22 To improve your voice's _____ , tighten and relax your jaws, yawn, and exercise shoulder and neck muscles.

2.23 The level at which your voice operates with the greatest ease is your _____

_____ .

2.24 To insure that your audience hears every syllable, speak _____ .

2.25 Perfect your facial expressions and gestures by _____

_____ .

2.26 Try to establish _____ contact with your audience.

2.27 Some standard markings for noting phrasing and emphasis in a speech are a. _____ , which indicates a short pause; b. _____ , which indicates a longer pause; and c. _____ , which indicates that the d. _____ word is stressed or emphasized.

Complete this speech activity.

2.28 Revise your literary critique until you think it would make an interesting speech. Practice it at least once a day for four days using the preceding advice. Then, deliver it to at least five classmates. Ask their opinion of your delivery and ask whether or not they have understood and learned from your critique. Write your findings on these lines.

_____

_____

_____

_____

_____

_____

_____

_____

TEACHER CHECK _____ _____

initials   date

READING LITERATURE TO AN AUDIENCE

Reading literature aloud requires an additional skill, the ability to cut literature. You should use for your reading only interesting passages that can be read to an audience in the time you are allowed. Careless cutting can destroy the author's intent or can confuse listeners who need more details. You should probably avoid cutting poetry at all; select poems short enough to fit your time limitations. In cutting plays or prose, follow these guidelines (more details can be found in Language Arts 1007, Section 1):

1. Select a key passage that represents the theme of the whole work and that will need as little explanation as possible; make certain that it can stand alone.

2. Use large segments whenever possible.

3. Cut out minor characters if they do not advance the plot or affect the outcome of your reading.

4. Eliminate unnecessary description, stage directions, or scenes that depend on lighting and sound effects.

5. Make certain that your cutting has not distorted the author's purpose.

After you are satisfied with your cutting, you may need to prepare an introduction. Give any background information necessary, fill in any important details, and set the mood for the literature that you intend to interpret.

Answer the following questions.

2.29 How should poetry be cut?

_____

_____

2.30 Why should minor characters be cut?

_____

_____

2.31 Should you use a large segment whenever possible, or several short segments of literature for your oral interpretation? Why?

_____

_____

_____

_____

_____

Complete the following activity.

2.32 Choose a key scene from the play *Everyman* (in Language Arts 1007) and cut it until it can be read in two minutes. Type it or copy it carefully marking passages and words with the symbols reviewed. Give your reading to at least five classmates. Have them evaluate your reading using the following questions:

 1. Is the purpose of the cutting clear?

 2. Is the action easy to follow or confusing?

 3. Are the characters interesting or are there too many to follow?

 4. Does the cutting start in an interesting, straightforward place?

 5. Does the cutting end in a logical, satisfying place?

Summarize your classmate's reactions on the lines. Staple your marked copy of *Everyman* to this page.

_____

_____

_____

_____

_____

_____

_____

_____

_____

_____

_____

_____

_____

_____

_____

_____

TEACHER CHECK _____ _____
                                  initials   date

LISTENING TO WHAT IS SAID

Now that you are aware of the work and planning involved in writing and delivering a speech, you realize that listeners have a responsibility to pay close attention to a speech. Careful listening shows appreciation for the speaker's hard work It also enables you to understand and retain essential information given in church school, social, and professional groups.

Critical listening involves not only attention and concentration, but also a mental evaluation of attitudes and the reliability of information. The following steps should enable you to understand and evaluate a speech (more details are available in Language Arts 1002, Section 3):

1. *Listen for the main ideas* outlined in the introduction, repeated throughout the speech, and summarized in the conclusion. Make certain that the ideas have been supported and that the conclusion is logical.

2. *Outline the main ideas* either mentally or on paper. Do not write down entire sentences or you will be too preoccupied with writing to listen. Fill in the details of your outline after the speech is over.

3. *Listen for key words* that signal changes in subject or support. These words are transitions you have reviewed in the section on paragraphs in this LIFEPAC; a thorough list is in Section 3 of Language Arts 1002.

4. *Take notes critically* by fitting together ideas *mentally* and writing down only those words that will help you to remember relationships. However, you may want to write down the speaker's exact words if you intend to quote him.

5. *Weigh the evidence.* Learn to make these distinctions:

   a. Are the speaker's points supported by *facts or opinions*? Facts should be supported by an outside authority such as a careful study having statistics, dates, knowledgeable people, or other details.

   b. Is the speaker an *authority* in the area on which they are speaking?

   c. Does the speaker give enough evidence for each point? One isolated example or one opinion is probably not adequate support.

   d. Is the speaker's argument logical? Does it follow from all his evidence, or does it seem to have been forced?

 Write the letter of the correct answer on each line.

2.33 In a speech, main ideas are often outlined _____ .
   a. on the blackboard before the speech begins
   b. at the conclusion of a speech
   c. on sheets of paper handed out at the same time as the speech is given
   d. both in the introduction and in the conclusion

2.34 When you take notes for a speech, _____ .

    a. write down everything quickly
    b. write down complete sentences
    c. write down only main ideas
    d. write down details hurriedly; you can supply the main ideas later

2.35 Which two of the following examples are facts? _____

    a. Dogs kill sheep.
    b. I've heard that dogs have been killing sheep.
    c. Two neighbors and I saw Eliot's dog kill a sheep.
    d. A recent survey of sheep farmers revealed that 100,000 sheep were killed by dogs last year.

2.36 Which two of the following examples are authorities whose speeches should be reliable?

_____

    a. a medical doctor speaking about smoking
    b. a medical doctor speaking about oil shortages
    c. an army general speaking about health insurance
    d. an army general speaking about the weapons race

Complete this evaluation activity.

2.37 Listen again to a classmate's literary critique. Using the critical listening suggestions, evaluate the critique. Discuss your evaluation with the speaker.

    a. What are the main points? _____

    _____

    b. Do those main points make sense? Are they supported with examples and facts?

    _____

    c. Are the main points easy to understand and follow? _____

    _____

    d. Do you trust the speaker's judgment? _____

    _____

TEACHER CHECK _____ _____

                                                       initials   date

Review the material in this section in preparation for the Self Test. The Self Test will check your mastery of this section as well as your knowledge of the previous section. The items missed will indicate specific areas where restudy is needed for mastery.

SELF TEST 2

Answer *true* **or** *false* (each answer, 1 point).

2.01 _____ You should choose a speech topic that makes you angry enough to say what you think.

2.02 _____ You should choose a speech topic about which you are informed.

2.03 _____ You should use a subject, examples, and a level of usage that are appropriate for your audience.

2.04 _____ In your outline use Roman numerals for supporting details and examples.

2.05 _____ Clichés are often helpful in getting an audience's interest.

2.06 _____ Use a formal level of usage for all audiences.

2.07 _____ All the forms of the novel can be easily listed.

2.08 _____ Test your speech by making a recording of it.

2.09 _____ Take deep breaths supported with lower muscles so that you can relax and have enough air to phrase words properly.

2.010 _____ Always use the same pitch.

Match these items (each answer, 2 points).

2.011 _____ amplification of the voice

2.012 _____ level at which voice operates with the greatest ease

2.013 _____ time sequence

2.014 _____ sayings that have lost their meaning

2.015 _____ tone, the highness and lowness of the voice

a. connotations
b. clichés
c. resonance
d. pitch
e. optimum pitch
f. chronological order
g. comparison/contrast order

Write the letter for the correct answer on each line (each answer, 2 points).

2.016 Adjectives used in a paper should be _____ .
   a. descriptive and general
   b. inappropriate and general
   c. necessary and numerous
   d. necessary and specific

2.017 The level of usage to use for academic writing is _____ .
a. formal
b. semi-formal
c. slang
d. informal

2.018 If you are stiff and too nervous to look at your audience during your speech, _____ .
a. raise your pitch and hug your body
b. yawn and tighten your jaw
c. take a few steps and stare at the floor
d. take a few steps and look slightly above your audience

2.019 The mark that is not standard for marking pauses and emphasis in a speech is _____ .
a. ~   b. /   c. //   d. (word)

2.020 When preparing literature for an oral interpretation, you should _____ .
a. select a key passage that can stand alone
b. select a passage with as many characters as possible
c. select several short passages to paste together
d. select a passage with much description or narration

Complete these sentences (each answer, 3 points).

2.021 A sentence that contains at least two independent clauses is a(n) _____

_____ .

2.022 Word endings that indicate words' grammatical functions are called _____ .

2.023 Verbals used only as adjectives are _____ .

2.024 An antecedent is a word for which a(n) _____ stands.

2.025 A reflexive pronoun is a word ending in _____ that refers to the previously used noun or pronoun.

2.026 An etymology is the _____ of a word.

2.027 Nonrestrictive clauses are _____ to the meaning of the words modified and are set off by commas.

2.028 Gerunds are verbals ending in _____ and are used only as nouns.

2.029 As you listen to a speaker, you should weigh the argument by deciding whether it is supported with facts or just with _____ .

2.030 In a speech, difficult words should either be defined or _____ .

Correct these sentences by underlining the error and writing the correction on the line following each sentence (each numbered item, 3 points).

2.031 Always avoid wordyness in writing a descriptive passage. _____

2.032 The man whom is entering that room should be stopped. _____

2.033 "Johnny, did you put that hamster back in it's cage?" Linda asked. _____

2.034 The room was dark; George couldn't hardly find the light switch. _____

2.035 Having found the chemical on the table.

_____

Complete these exercises (each answer, 5 points).

2.036 List two ways in which a speech can be made suitable for a particular kind of audience.

_____

_____

_____

2.037 Tell why a speaker would want to place marks on a speech.

_____

_____

2.038 List two things to remember in cutting literature for an oral interpretation.

_____

_____

_____

2.039 At what position should you listen for the main ideas of a speech?

_____

_____

2.040 List two ways in which a listener should judge a speaker's speech.

_____

_____

_____

_____

80 / 100

SCORE _____ **TEACHER** _____ _____
                                              initials   date

3. READING

At this point in your review, you might feel that you have already covered the difficult, active part of your study of English. After all, you might reason, you have been reading for years; what can be so difficult about reading? Yet, you probably remember reading something, pausing, and realizing that you could not recall one idea from what you had just read. Just as you as listener must listen carefully for main points in a speech, you as reader must search for meaning in your reading. Moreover, you must be critical.

You must examine what you read as carefully as you evaluate what you hear. Reading for and writing a literary critique should have convinced you that printed material is not always well written or true. Reading, then, is an active, difficult job; you must constantly find major points and evaluate their truth and the skill with which they are written.

Section Objectives

Review these objectives. When you have completed this section, you should be able to:

9. Identify the major points in reading material.
10. Explain some elements of poetry and interpret poems.
11. Identify the characters and structure of the drama *Everyman*.
12. Explain some elements of three short stories.
13. Discuss the novel, *In His Steps,* using the skills acquired in this series.

Vocabulary

Study these words to enhance your learning success in this section.

alliteration	miracle play	rhyme scheme
concrete images	morality play	theme
frame story	onomatopoeia	tragic hero
logical fallacies	point of view	

READING FOR MEANING

As you read, you should be alert to clues to the meaning of a piece of writing. The title and introduction should immediately give you an idea of the **theme** of a literary work. Then you must concentrate on individual paragraphs to decide how they support or develop this theme.

You have reviewed the importance of giving each of your own paragraphs a definite purpose usually summarized in a topic sentence. Understanding the structure of a paragraph should enable you to read other authors' paragraphs with greater appreciation and efficiency. Remember to concentrate on the purpose of each paragraph by finding the topic sentence or the overall purpose.

Titles, introductions, and topic sentences all offer valuable clues to the meaning of a piece of writing. The following list should give you additional suggestions for reading carefully (a detailed discussion may be found in Language Arts 1006, Section 3):

1. *Key words that are unfamiliar* to you may sometimes be solved by searching for adjectives that describe the words, or for appositives or clauses that may explain difficult words. Use a dictionary whenever necessary.

2. *Main ideas* in writing often become more obvious when you become aware of the *overall structure* of the work. Usually a writer will use one of six types if the work is expository (illustration/example, comparison/contrast, cause and effect, definition, classification or division and process analysis).

3. *Chapter titles* in the table of contents often give clues to structure and meaning.

4. The author's *tone* (attitude toward the subject) helps the reader to infer the author's purpose (is the writer serious, formal, playful, intimate, or condescending?).

 Read the following paragraphs and complete the activities by writing the letter of the correct answer on the line.

3.1 *Writing is difficult because so many skills are involved. We must spell and form words correctly, and we must arrange sentences clearly. We must construct paragraphs logically, and we must pull paragraphs together so that they work to form a unified piece of writing. All of these skills require frequent review, careful examination, and practice.*

What is the topic sentence of this paragraph? _____
a. Writing is difficult because so many skills are involved.
b. We must spell and form words correctly, and we must arrange sentences clearly.
c. We must construct paragraphs logically, and we must pull paragraphs together so that they work to form a unified piece of writing.
d. All these skills require review, careful examination, and practice.

3.2 *For the night-wind has a dismal trick of wandering round and round a building of that sort, and moaning as it goes; and of trying, with its unseen hand, the windows and the doors; and seeking out some crevices by which to enter. And when it has got in; as one not finding what it seeks, whatever that may be, it wails and howls to issue forth again: and not content with stalking through the aisles, and gliding round and round the pillars, and tempting the deep organ, soars up to the roof, and strives to rend the rafters: then flings itself despairingly upon the stones below, and passes, muttering, into the vaults. Anon, it comes up stealthily, and creeps along the walls, seeming to read, in whispers, the Inscriptions sacred to the Dead. At some of these, it breaks out shrilly, as with laughter; and at others, moans and cries as if it were lamenting. It has a ghostly sound too, lingering with the altar; where it seems to chaunt, in its wild way, of Wrong and Murder done, and false Gods worshipped, in defiance of the Tables of the Law, which look so fair and smooth, but are so flawed and broken....It has an awful voice, that wind at Midnight, singing in a church!* (from "The Chimes," First Quarter, by Charles Dickens)

What is the main idea of this paragraph? _____
a. Murderers are buried in some churches.
b. Ghosts haunt churches at midnight.
c. The wind moans like a restless ghost as it sings in a church at midnight.
d. Churches are drafty and open to midnight winds during choir rehearsals.

3.3 *A prison taint was on everything there. The imprisoned air, the imprisoned light, the imprisoned damps, the imprisoned men, were all deteriorated by confinement. As the captive men were faded and haggard, so the iron was rusty, the stone was slimy, the wood was rotten, the air was faint, the light was dim. Like a well, like a vault, like a tomb, the prison had no knowledge of the brightness outside; and would have kept its polluted atmosphere intact, in one of the spice islands of the Indian ocean.* (from *Little Dorrit*, Book the First, chapter 1, by Charles Dickens)

What is the main idea of this paragraph? _____
a. The prison was dark and empty.
b. The prison was on one of the spice islands.
c. "A prison taint was on everything there."
d. "The prison had no knowledge of the brightness outside."

3.4 *She knew now what meant the duties of the household, the heavy work of the kitchen. Her pretty hands soon lost all semblance of the care of bygone days. She washed the soiled linen and dried it in her room. She went every morning to the street with the refuse of the kitchen, carrying the water, stopping at each flight of stairs to take breath—wearing the dress of the women of the people; she went each day to the grocer, the fruiterer, the butcher, carrying her basket on her arm, bargaining, defending cent by cent her miserable money.*
(from "The Necklace," by Guy de Maupassant)

What is the topic sentence of this paragraph? _____
a. She knew now what meant the duties of the household, the heavy work of the kitchen.
b. Her pretty hands soon lost all semblance of the care of bygone days.
c. She washed the soiled linen and dried it in her room.
d. She defended cent by cent her miserable money.

Read the sentences and answer the questions without using a dictionary.
When you have finished check your answers in a dictionary.

a. His *xenophobia* caused him to avoid the stranger.
b. He put his shirt in a large leather *portmanteau*.
c. The *vagabond*, exhausted and covered with dust, went to a third house to ask directions.

3.5   What do you think *xenophobia* means?

_____

3.6   What would you guess a *portmanteau* is?

_____

3.7   What is a *vagabond*?

_____

Read the following paragraphs and complete the activities.

A verbal may belong to one of three categories. It may be a participle, which is used only as an adjective. It may be a gerund, which always ends in -ing and functions as a noun. Finally, it may be an infinitive, which is preceded by to and functions as a noun, adjective, or even an adverb. Yet verbals still look very much like verbs.

3.8   Which one of the six types of expository structure does this paragraph illustrate?

_____

3.9   Write the supporting points of this paragraph.

_____

_____

_____

3.10 This paragraph outlines _____ classes.

Writing is difficult because so many skills are involved. We must spell and form words correctly, and we must arrange sentences clearly. We must construct paragraphs logically, and we must pull paragraphs together so that they work to form a unified piece of writing. All these skills require frequent review, careful examination, and practice.

3.11 What type of expository structure was used for this paragraph?

_____

3.12 Are the supporting sentences important categories or simply examples to support the topic sentence? _____

The Puritan writers John Milton and John Bunyan had much in common. Milton was imprisoned for his support of the Commonwealth. He had difficulties supporting his large family, and yet wrote a brilliant epic. In the same way, Bunyan was imprisoned, impoverished, and yet strengthened to write a great allegory.

3.13 What type of expository structure was used to write this paragraph?

_____

3.14 Is there a close relationship between Milton and Bunyan in this paragraph?

_____

_____

_____

3.15 How many points of comparison are made? _____

Read the following passages and complete the activities by writing the letter of the correct answer on each blank.

In the beginnings of the last chapter, I informed you exactly when I was born; but I did not inform you how. No; that particular was reserved entirely for a chapter by itself; besides, Sir, as you and I are in a manner perfect strangers to each other, it would not have been proper to have let you into too many circumstances relating to myself all at once.—You must have a little patience. I have undertaken, you see, to write not only my life, but my opinions also; hoping and expecting that your knowledge of my character, and of what kind of a mortal I am, by the one, would give you a better relish for the other: As you proceed further with me, the slight acquaintance which is now beginning betwixt us, will grow into familiarity; and that, unless one of us is in fault, will terminate in friendship. (from Tristram Shandy, *Volume I, Chapter 6, by Laurence Sterne)*

3.16 The tone of this passage is _____ .
a. formal (distant) and stiff
b. intimate (chatty) and playful
c. condescending and formal
d. serious and intimate

3.17 This tone should indicate that _____ .
a. several major points are here
b. nothing is important here
c. the details help us to understand the speaker
d. the details are unnecessary

She [Becky] made her preparations for departure...and accepted all the kind little Amelia's presents, after just the proper degree of hesitation and reluctance...Finally came the parting with Miss Amelia, over which picture I intend to throw a veil. But after a scene in which one person was in earnest and the other a perfect performer—after the tenderest carresses, the most pathetic tears, the smelling-bottle, and some of the very best feelings of the heart, had been called into requisition—Rebecca and Amelia parted, the former vowing to love her friend for ever and ever and ever. (from *Vanity Fair*, Chapter VI, by William Makepeace Thackeray)

3.18 The tone of this passage _____ .
   a. is serious
   b. is intimate
   c. means something deeper than what is said
   d. talks to the reader in a belittling way

3.19 The author is really saying this about Becky: _____ .
   a. that she loves Amelia with all her heart
   b. that she is only pretending to love Amelia
   c. that she is a professional actress
   d. that she is taking a trip to Australia

Cause-and-effect relationships should be examined carefully. They often appear in essays to convince readers that certain causes will have certain effects. They also appear in fictional stories to explain why certain characters behave the way they do, or why certain events happened in the plot. You should be alert to **logical fallacies**, false acts of reasoning, which do not present true relationships between causes and their effects (results).

To check a cause-and-effect relationship, *check the cause* in the following ways:

1. Make certain that the cause is able to produce the effect.

2. Make certain that if the cause is gone, the effect will be gone.

3. Make certain that if the cause is introduced in a similar situation, it will produce a similar effect.

Some common *mistakes* made in presenting cause-and-effect relationships are these:

1. Thinking that A causes B because A always comes before B (saying that Bethany causes rain because rain always falls on every picnic to which Bethany has come),

2. Mistaking an effect for a cause (saying a sore throat makes you weak), or

3. Oversimplifying the cause (saying sponsors are not tolerant of class activities because they are older).

| The moon's gravitational pull causes tides on Earth.

 Explain the faulty reasoning in the following statements; some statements may be correct.

3.20 Women are terrible drivers; my aunt has had three automobile accidents.

_____

3.21 I inherited my poor spelling ability from my parents.

_____

_____

3.22 I'm bringing my blue fountain pen to the speech contest; I never forget my speech when

I have my pen. _____

3.23 Charles Dickens wrote about the poor because he himself had lived with and observed the poor and because he was sensitive to human suffering.

_____

3.24 The pudding tastes scorched because I forgot to stir it and allowed it to boil too long.

_____

READING AND EXPERIENCING POETRY

Poetry was enjoyed hundreds of years before novels or short stories, yet modern readers often prefer to read novels or short stories. Many readers claim they do not have the time to solve compact lines of poetry. They also prefer a fast moving plot rather than the slow, thorough examination of emotions and characters found in poetry. Some readers believe, however, that poetry is worth the extra reading time because its appeal is usually to emotions.

Elements of poetry. Poetry can be recognized by its compactness of thought, its use of **concrete images**, and its personal effect. Its overall effect is unique to each reader or listener; thus, that effect is greater than the sum of the concrete images. Poetry can also be recognized by a number of additional poetic elements. Not all of these elements are always present in the same poem, but many appear together. Reviewing these elements of poetry should enable you to enjoy a poet's skill more readily. (If necessary, review Language Arts 1004, Section 2, for details.)

1. *Diction*, the careful use of words, is especially important in poetry.

   a. *Denotations*—Be thoroughly aware of the literal definitions of words even words that you think you understand. Use the dictionary to help you to find more than one meaning for the same word; the poet may have intended several meanings to apply so that the poem can examine a wider area of experience.

   b. *Connotations*—Be aware of the atmosphere caused by the ideas, sensations, and images associated with words. The word castle, for example, may have the simple denotative meaning of a large, protected building, but the word *suggests* knights, armor, tournaments, romance, and dungeons.

   c. *Levels of usage*—Be prepared to solve the more formal usage of older poetry. Although that poetic diction may contain structures and words no longer used, the emotions described are as real today as they were when the poem was written.

2. *Meter*, the arrangement and repetition of beats or accents in a line of poetry, is a strictly controlled rhythm that pleases the ears and aids in our memory of lines.

   a. *Types of feet*—Scan (mark) the feet by using the symbol ' above stressed syllables, ˘, above unstressed syllables, and / to divide feet. The mark // indicates a pause within a line. The rhythm of the feet should agree with the natural accents of words and phrases.

      i. *Iambic* is a unit of meter having an unaccented syllable followed by an accented syllable (˘').

      ii. *Trochaic* is a unit of meter having an accented syllable followed by an unaccented syllable ('˘).

      iii. *Dactylic* is a unit of meter having an accented syllable followed by two unaccented syllables ('˘˘).

      iv. *Anapestic* is a unit of meter having two unaccented syllables followed by an accented syllable (˘˘').

    b.   *Determine the number of fee*t within a line.

       i.   *Dimeter* is a line of two feet; this line is read very quickly.

      ii.   *Trimeter* is a line of three feet; it is also read quickly.

     iii.   *Tetrameter* is a line of four feet.

     iv.   *Pentameter* is a line of five feet, the most common line in English poetry.

      v.   *Hexameter* is a line of six feet.

     vi.   *Heptameter* is a line of seven feet; it is read slowly.

3.   *Rhyme and other sound effects* make poetry especially suitable for oral interpretation.

    a.   Determine the **rhyme scheme** by assigning the same letter of the alphabet to each example of similar sounds. Rhymes please the ear and tie together lines that form thought units.

       i.   A *couplet* is a unit of two lines of verse with similar end-rhymes.

      ii.   A *sonnet* has fourteen lines and may either have a rhyme scheme such as *abba abba cdcdcd* (Italian) or *abab cdcd efefgg* (English).

    b.   Recognize **onomatopoeia** by words that sound like the noise that they describe.

    c.   Recognize **alliteration** by the repetition of initial consonants that imitate the sounds being described or that emphasize lines.

4.   *Figures of speech* are various uses of words that depart from the literal meanings of those words.

    a.   A *simile* is a stated comparison using the words *like* or *as*.

    b.   A *metaphor* is an implied comparison, a comparison that is *not* stated.

    c.   A *symbol* is something that stands for something else in addition to its literal meaning. It may be universal (or commonly understood), such as the Cross, or it may be personal.

    d.   *Personification* gives human characteristics to inanimate objects, ideas, or animals.

    e.   An *apostrophe* is a sudden, direct address to an inanimate object, an abstract quality, or a fictitious person.

    f.   To use *metonymy* is to use a word as a substitute for another word that is associated with it.

    g.   To use *irony* is to give the appearance of saying one thing while meaning something else.

    h.   A *hyperbole* is an exaggeration of fact used for poetic effect.

    i.   An *understatement* deliberately represents something as less than it is.

    j.   A *paradox* is a statement that seems false but may actually be true.

5.   The *imagery* of a poem is the collection of images, vivid descriptions that appeal to the five senses.

    a.   Sight images (sometimes called *visual* images) appeal to the eyes.

    b.   Sound images (sometimes called *auditory*) appeal to the ears.

    c.   Smell images (sometimes called *olfactory*) appeal to the nose.

    d.   Taste images (sometimes called *gustatory*) appeal to our sense of taste.

    e.   Touch images (sometimes called *tactile*) appeal to our sense of touch.

Match the following items without consulting the above outline.

3.25 _____ the arrangement of beats or accents in a line of poetry

3.26 _____ the pattern in which similar end-sounds occur in a poem

3.27 _____ a unit of meter having an unaccented syllable followed by an accented syllable

3.28 _____ a unit of meter having an accented syllable followed by an unaccented syllable

3.29 _____ the use of words that sound like the noises they describe

3.30 _____ the repetition of consonants at the beginning of words

3.31 _____ a stated comparison using *like* or *as*

3.32 _____ an implied (unstated) comparison

3.33 _____ something that stands for something else

3.34 _____ gives human characteristics to inanimate objects, ideas, and animals

3.35 _____ giving the appearance of saying one thing while meaning something else

3.36 _____ a sudden, direct address to an inanimate object, an abstract quality, or a fictitious person

a. iambic foot

b. onomatopoeia

c. apostrophe

d. meter

e. simile

f. rhyme scheme

g. trochaic foot

h. alliteration

i. metaphor

j. personification

k. symbol

l. irony

m. dactylic foot

Scan the following passage and answer the questions.

Willows whiten, aspens quiver,
Little breezes dusk and shiver
Thro' the wave that runs forever
By the island in the river
Flowing down to Camelot.
Four gray walls and four gray towers,
Overlook a space of flowers,
And the silent isle imbowers
The Lady of Shalott.

(from "The Lady of Shalott" by Alfred, Lord Tennyson)

3.37 The verb *whiten* in Line 1 is a very compressed image. It means that the wind turns the white underside of the willow leaves upward. In Line 2, the verb *dusk* is used in an unusual way. Locate that verb in the dictionary. What is its meaning

_____

3.38 Now locate the verb *shiver* in Line 2. Which definition seems to fit this use?

_____

3.39 Now the denotative meaning of Lines 1 through 3 should make more sense. What do the breezes do to the wave?

_____

_____

3.40 What connotations exist in the words *dusk* and *shiver*?

_____

3.41 In lines 1 through 8, what type of foot is used? _____

3.42 How many feet are in Lines 1 through 4?

_____

3.43 How many feet are in Line 9? _____

3.44 Why would a poet vary the number of feet in lines of poetry?

_____

3.45 What is the rhyme scheme of this passage? _____

3.46 Of what sound effect is "willows whiten" an example? _____

3.47 What images in the passage are visual?

_____

_____

_____

3.48 What images in the passage are auditory (can be heard)?

_____

_____

_____

Interpreting poetry. You have just reviewed a quite lengthy outline of the elements of poetry. To appreciate a poem completely, you certainly need to be aware of all those elements. Yet a poem is not a corpse dismembered on a table; it is a living work of art with various members or elements functioning together in a coordinated manner. Read a poem first for its *total meaning*. Then, appreciate it at its various levels of meaning.

Understanding the *literal meaning* of a poem is essential.

1. Be aware of every word's denotations; never read a poem without having a dictionary by your side.

2. Be aware of multiple meanings of words; the poet may have intended several meanings to apply.

3. Be aware of the connotations or atmospheres of words.

4. Make certain that you know what is happening; if the syntax (word arrangement) confuses you, rearrange the words mentally or on paper, if necessary, until you an identify the simple subjects, predicates, complements, and modifiers of every sentence.

In addition, you should recognize symbols, extended metaphors (metaphors used for longer periods), similes, and other figures of speech so that you can be aware of levels of meaning *beneath* the literal level.

Read the poem carefully and answer the questions.

Ars Poetica

A poem should be palpable and mute
As a globed fruit,

Dumb
As old medallions to the thumb,

Silent as the sleeve-worn stone
Of casement ledges where the moss has grown—

A poem should be wordless
As the flight of birds.

A poem should be motionless in time
As the moon climbs,

Leaving, as the moon releases
Twig by twig the night-entangled trees,

Leaving, as the moon behind the winter leaves,
Memory by memory the mind—

A poem should be motionless in time
As the moon climbs.

A poem should be equal to:
Not true.

For all the history of grief
An empty doorway and a maple leaf.

For love
The leaning grasses and two lights above the sea—

A poem should not mean
But be.

"Ars Poetica" by Archibald MacLeish reprinted by permission of Houghton Mifflin Company from *New & Collected Poems* 1917-1976
Copyright © 1976 by Archibald MacLeish

3.49 To what does the poet compare a poem and what type of comparison is made?

_____

_____

3.50 What do night and winter symbolize?

_____

_____

3.51 How does the moon escape time?

_____

_____

3.52 In the line "Leaving, as the moon behind the winter leaves," is the word *leaves* used as a noun or as a verb? _____

3.53 Why does the poet compare a poem to the moon?

_____

_____

Read the poem carefully and answer the questions.

Into my heart an air that kills
From yon far country blows:
What are those blue remembered hills,
What spires, what farms are those?

That is the land of lost content,
I see it shining plain,
The happy highways where I went
And cannot come again.

by A.E. Housman

3.54 What does the word *spires* mean? _____

3.55 What does the word *content* mean? _____

3.56 What does the word *plain* mean? _____

3.57 What is the speaker of the poem doing as he makes his observation?

_____

3.58 Why would the remembered hills be blue?

_____

3.59 What is the *literal* meaning of this poem?

_____

3.60 The quiet country to which the poet cannot return is a symbol of lost contentment.

How is the description of this land appropriate?_____

_____

3.61 Why were the highways happy? _____

3.62 A journey is often used as an extended metaphor of the passage of life itself, of our passing through time. Recognizing that possibility, how would you interpret the deeper or figurative meaning of the poem?

_____

_____

3.63 What is the rhyme scheme in each stanza? _____

3.64 What type of foot is used? _____

3.65 How many feet are in the first line? _____

3.66 How many feet are in the second? _____

3.67 Does this poem help you to recall some of your past experiences?
Write your impressions on the lines.

_____

_____

_____

READING DRAMA

The history of drama is old, going back to the ancient Greeks and Romans. Ancient Greek drama probably grew out of religious ceremonies. It is still worthwhile reading because of the insight of its playwrights and the use of conventions and types that have remained in some form in modern drama. Aeschylus, Sophocles, and Euripides were writers of tragedies, and Aristophanes was a writer of comedies. Few modern plays retain formal *prologues*, introductions to the main parts of plays, and *choruses*, groups commenting on the action. The following elements, however, have remained: *buffoons*, fools or pranksters; *puns*, plays on words based on the similarity of sounds between two words with different meanings; and *parodies*, humorous imitations of more serious works.

Tragedy as a form of drama has definitely remained. The **tragic hero**, although no longer regal, still suffers during the course of the play as the result of his flaw, weakness, or vice that prevents his ambitions from being fully achieved. The audience should still experience a *catharsis*, a satisfying "purge" of emotion, perhaps because the punished hero represents the audience's own problems and fears until they are resolved, or perhaps because the audience learns through the hero how to resolve its problems. Comedy, especially satiric comedy, has also remained as a form of modern drama.

As Greek drama declined Roman drama developed and often drew upon Greek sources. Seneca, a writer of tragedies, emphasized horror and included lengthy speeches. His plays greatly influenced Renaissance playwrights and probably began the tradition of the five-act play. Plautus and Terence, who wrote comedies, also influenced Renaissance playwrights. Performances of serious Greek and Roman plays ended, however, even before the decline of the Roman Empire. Romans then entertained themselves with decadent and often immoral farces, with pantomimes (stories told silently with gestures or dance), or with gladiators. As the church gained power, even these dramatic entertainments died. Just prior to the ninth century, only mimes, stories taken from classical plays and performed by wandering poets or musical performers, and folk-plays, usually about the four seasons, were presented to the public.

In the ninth century, the beginnings of public drama reappeared in church services as Latin dialogue dramatizing religious stories. The church, or *liturgical*, plays developed into **miracle plays** that were performed outside the church. These miracle plays included events of the Old and New Testaments and incidents in the lives of saints. In the twelfth century, plays were written and brought together to form *Cycles* in which combining short plays produced a long (one-to two-day) narrative on such topics as the Fall of Man, salvation, or Creation. Often, each play was held on a separate wagon that would be followed by another wagon and another play.

By the late fifteenth century, the **morality play** had developed. It differs from the miracle play because it is a dramatized allegory; virtues and vices appear in personified form to struggle for man's soul. Its purpose is to teach moral behavior rather than Biblical stories or stories about saints.

Answer *true* or *false*.

3.68 _____ Tragedy and comedy developed during Roman times.

3.69 _____ Greek playwrights used buffoons, puns, and parodies.

3.70 _____ The tragic hero usually has a tragic flaw.

3.71 _____ A catharsis is a type of comic character.

3.72 _____ Seneca is the least known Roman playwright.

3.73 _____ Romans continued to enjoy classical drama after the decline of the empire.

3.74 _____ Plays were not performed for several centuries.

3.75 _____ Drama reappeared in church services.

3.76 _____ A miracle play is about Biblical miracles.

3.77 _____ A morality play is a dramatized allegory.

The elements and features of drama. The elements of drama have developed throughout drama's history. Many writers believe that at least three elements must be present for a piece of writing to be considered drama:

1. Characters impersonated by actors;

2. A plot, a series of cause-and-effect actions; and

3. Dialogue, speeches spoken by the characters to each other.

Any of the following features *may* also be present:

1. A pyramid-like plot consisting of at least three parts: the *rising action*, the *climax*, and the *falling action* (most well-constructed tragedies have this plot arrangement);

2. A *soliloquy*, a character's speech spoken to himself while he is alone;

3. An *aside*, a character's speech spoken directly to the audience, unheard by the other characters;

4. *Dramatic irony*, the use of words or acts in a play that have meanings recognized by the audience, but unrecognized by the characters;

5. *Allegory*, a story in which characters, settings, and props represent parts of a doctrine (teaching) or theme (universal truth or abstract concept).

Match the items.

3.78 _____	a character speaking to the audience	a. dramatic irony
3.79 _____	a character speaking to himself	b. tragedy
3.80 _____	the audience knows something the characters do not know	c. soliloquy
		d. aside
3.81 _____	a story in which characters represent parts of a teaching	e. allegory
3.82 _____	a form of drama having a pyramid like structure	f. comedy

Answer the following questions.

3.83 What are the three divisions of a tragedy's plot?

a. _____

b. _____

c. _____

3.84 What three elements are necessary for a play?

a. _____

b. _____

c. _____

Everyman. *Everyman* is a late fifteenth-century English morality play. It is an allegory. At a literal level, it is the story of Everyman's journey as he is forsaken by some characters and is finally comforted by others. At the allegorical level, it teaches the doctrine of salvation. The characters also work at two levels; they have personal characteristics, but they are also personifications of vices, virtues, mental qualities, and groups of friends and relatives.

This structural outline should enable you to review the plot of the play (if any portion of the outline is unfamiliar, review *Everyman* in Language Arts 1007, Section 3):

1. *Initial situation*—God is displeased with Everyman's ingratitude and selfishness.

2. *Initial action*—God sends Death to Everyman with a command that Everyman take a journey (toward death) and bring his account book with him (for the last judgment).

3. *Rising action*—Everyman says his first soliloquy while realizing that he is alone. He says his second soliloquy after Fellowship has left him. After Kindred, Cousin, and Goods forsake him, Everyman decides in his third soliloquy that no one will come with him but his Good Deeds. Since Good Deeds is too weak to travel, her sister Knowledge brings Everyman to Confession.

4. *Climax*—Everyman asks forgiveness for his sins. Good Deeds is healed when Everyman is no longer concerned with the pleasures of the body. Everyman puts on the garment of contrition. Discretion, Strength, Beauty, and Five Wits join Everyman.

5. *Falling action*—The group approaches the grave. Beauty leaves rather than smother in the grave; Strength and Discretion also go. Five Wits departs; then, Knowledge, but she is no longer needed. Good Deeds, however, accompanies Everyman into the grave.

 Answer the following questions.

3.85 What role would each of these characters play in Everyman's journey?

a. Discretion _____

_____

b. Strength _____

_____

c. Beauty _____

_____

d. Five Wits _____

_____

3.86 How is Everyman's aging and dying realistically portrayed?

_____

_____

_____

3.87 Why are the following lines central to the play?

All earthly things is but vanity.
Beauty, Strength, and Discretion do man forsake,
Foolish friends and kinsmen, that fair spake,
All fleeth save Good Deeds....

_____

_____

_____

_____

_____

3.88 Fellowship speaks the following words:

Sir, I must needs know your heaviness;
I have pity to see you in any distress;
If any have you wronged, ye shall revenged be,
Though I on the ground be slain for thee,
Though that I know before that I should die.

Does he, in fact, remain with Everyman? _____

3.89 Goods utters these words to Everyman.

But if thou had me loved moderately during,
As to the poor to give part of me,
Then shouldst thou not in this dolor be,
Nor in the great sorrow and care....
For when thou art dead, this is my guise,
Another to deceive in the same wise
As I have done thee, and all to his soul's reprief.

What does he mean by the last three lines?

_____

_____

_____

_____

3.90 Good Deeds says:

Here I lie, cold in the ground...
Everyman, I am sorry of your fall,
And fain would I help you, and I were able.

Why were Everyman's Good Deeds so weak?

_____

_____

_____

READING SHORT STORIES

A short story is a brief fictional narrative (sequence of events) in prose. It usually can be read at one sitting. Most of the time it deals with a single problem or idea, has a single plot, and brings about a single effect. Finally, characters in a short story are revealed through their own actions.

Nearly all short stories have the following elements in common (for more details, consult Language Arts 1008, Section 1:

1. *Setting* is the short story's specific location and time.
   a. Setting may create a *mood* with words having definite connotations and with descriptions that appeal to the five senses (careful writers do not use unnecessary details, however).
   b. Setting may reveal *character* by allowing objects to reflect a character's personality.
2. *Characters* in short stories are revealed by their *actions* and their *speech*; in addition, the author sometimes gives telling statements about certain characters or allows the reader to know his attitude toward them. Short story characters usually do not change their own behavior because a short story rarely has the space for that sort of development.
   a. The *protagonist* is the main character.
   b. An *antagonist* is a character who may oppose the main character.
3. *Conflict* is the struggle that ends in the protagonist's success or defeat.
   a. An *external conflict* is a struggle between the protagonist and someone or something outside himself.
   b. An *internal conflict* is a struggle taking place within the protagonist.
4. *Plot* is the series of events that bring the conflict to an end. In a short story, the plot usually can be divided into the following sections:
   a. the *rising action*, the incidents leading up to the climax;
   b. the *climax*, the point of the greatest emotional impact in which the action ends and the reader sees how the conflict will be resolved (this point usually comes quite near the end of a short story); and
   c. the *denouement*, the last few sentences or paragraphs that end the story.
5. The *theme* is the main idea of the story; it can usually be expressed in one sentence.

The elements listed are fairly obvious in a short story if you read it carefully. However, the approach to the short story, the point from which the author presents the story, may not be so noticeable to you; you may simply take it for granted.

Nevertheless, this **point of view** plays a very important role in determining how much information is told to the reader. The following points of view are described in Language Arts 1008, Section 1:

1. *First person*, using pronouns *I, me, we, mine, ours, myself, ourselves*, the narrator may be a main character or a minor character; and he may understand what he observes; or he may misunderstand events.

2. *Second person*, using pronouns *you, yours, yourself*, is rarely used in short stories.

3. *Third person*, using the pronouns *he, she, they, it, his, hers, their, its, himself, herself, themselves, itself*, may either be all-knowing or somewhat limited in knowledge of details.

Complete the following statements.

3.91 A reader learns to know short story characters by their a. _____ and

b. _____ .

3.92 The protagonist is the _____ .

3.93 The character who opposes the protagonist is the _____ .

3.94 A trapper struggling to survive a hard winter is experiencing a(n) _____ conflict.

3.95 The rising action ends, and the reader experiences the greatest emotional impact of the story at the _____ of the story.

3.96 The setting may set the a. _____ of the story, or it may reveal something about a character's b. _____ .

Answer the following questions.

3.97 What are three characteristics of a short story?

a. _____

b. _____

c. _____

3.98 What are the five elements most short stories have in common.

a. _____   b. _____

c. _____   d. _____

e. _____

Read the passage carefully and answer the questions by writing the letter of the correct answer on each line.

She was such a sharp little lady, and used to sit with her hands folded in each other, looking so very watchful while she talked to me that perhaps I found that rather irksome. Or perhaps it was her being so upright and trim; though I don't think it was that, because I thought that quaintly pleasant. Nor can it have been the general expression of her face, which was very sparkling and pretty for an old lady. I don't know what it was. Or at least if I do, now, I thought I did not then. Or at least—but it don't matter. (from *Bleak House*, Chapter XXX, by Charles Dickens)

3.99   What is the point of view of this passage? _____

    a. first person   b. second person   c. third person   d. no person

3.100   What is the narrator saying? _____

    a. that she is ill
    b. that the old lady is ill
    c. that the old lady made her feel uncomfortable
    d. that the old lady made her forget her troubles

3.101   How would the use of another point of view have changed the passage? _____

    a. Another point of view would have left out the old lady.
    b. Another point of view would have left out the narrator.
    c. Another point of view would probably have lengthened the passage.
    d. Another point of view would probably have shortened the passage and stated the problem directly.

3.102   How do the last three sentences contribute to the passage? _____

    a. They help to characterize the narrator as someone too kind and shy to admit that she disliked someone.
    b. They add valuable details to the plot.
    c. They help characterize the old lady as someone unkind and unfair.
    d. They have no value at all.

Answer this question.

3.103   Do you think the point of view used is suitable? Would you have used that point of view to say the same thing? Why? Why not?

_____

_____

_____

_____

_____

TEACHER CHECK _____ _____

                                                initials   date

The Celebrated Jumping frog of Calaveras County. The following breakdown of Mark Twain's short story, first published in 1865, should enable you to review the story's basic structure. For further review, consult Language Arts 1008, Section 1.

1. *Setting*—Angel Camp, a California gold camp;
2. *Characters*—Jim Smiley, the stranger, Simon Wheeler, and the teller of the story (the narrator);
3. *Conflict*—between Jim Smiley and the stranger; and, in a different way, between Simon Wheeler and the narrator (who is annoyed that Simon Wheeler cannot get to the point of his story);
4. *Plot*—Simon Wheeler tells the narrator about Jim Smiley's gambling ventures and especially about Jim's frog Dan'l Webster, which lost a race when a stranger filled him full of quail shot;
5. *Theme or focus*—this story does not actually have a theme, but it does offer a study of two characters, the gambler Jim Smiley, and the talkative Simon Wheeler;
6. *Point of view*—the whole story is-told by an unknown narrator in first person point of view—the **frame story** is told in third person (Simon tells about Jim); and
7. Special devices:
    a. *Frame story*—The overall narrator, an outsider to Simon's and Jim's circle of friends, presents Simon Wheeler's story about Jim Smiley;
    b. *Dialect*—Simon Wheeler's speech pattern is not standard, but is that of a mining community;
    c. *Similes and metaphors*—Simon uses humorous and descriptive comparisons to make his story realistic; and
    d. *Personification*—Simon describes Jim's trained animals as if they were human.

Answer the following questions, reviewing more of the short story if necessary.

3.104 With what point of view does the story begin? _____

3.105 Does the narrator describe Simon Wheeler? _____

_____

3.106 Does Simon Wheeler take his story seriously? _____

_____

3.107 What do you know about Simon Wheeler from his speech? _____

_____

3.108 What do the little incidents about the mare and the pup named Andrew Jackson tell you about Simon Wheeler's story telling? _____

_____

3.109 What is the climax of this story? _____

_____

3.110 How does the denouncement come about? _____

_____

Complete this activity.

In Language Arts 1008 you studied two other short stories, "The Lady or the Tiger?" by Frank R. Stockton and "The Necklace" by Guy de Maupassant. Choose *one* of these stories and complete the following breakdown for that story. If you need to reread the story, go back to Language Arts 1008 and reread it.

3.111 *Setting* _____

_____

3.112 *Characters* _____

_____

3.113 *Conflict* _____

_____

3.114 *Plot* _____

_____

_____

_____

_____

3.115 *Theme* _____

_____

3.116 *Point of View* _____

_____

Answer the questions that apply to the story you have just outlined.

"The Lady or the Tiger"

3.117 What is the climax of the story? _____

_____

3.118 What is your understanding of the princess's character? _____

_____

3.119 What kind of person would the princess have to be to prevent her young man's death?

_____

_____

"The Necklace"

3.120 How would you describe Madame Loisel at the beginning of the story?

_____

_____

_____

_____

3.121 How has Madame Loisel changed at the end of the story?

_____

READING A NOVEL

Only recently has the novel become a respected literary form. Several reasons account for slow acceptance by some critics. Probably the main reason is that the novel has developed to its present form too quickly for conservative critics. Although several qualities present in novels are also in some ancient and medieval works, the complex combinations now found in the novel do not appear until the eighteenth century.

In addition, some critics have considered the novelist's use of realistic details inferior to the poet's and dramatist's use of rigid structure and economical language. Such critics have been unable to realize the artistic complexity and social value of novels, but the reading public, especially in the nineteenth century, has recognized and enjoyed novels as much as any written art form.

The novel, a long narrative of epic scope unified through plot, character, and theme, has continued drama's function of showing characters in action. Samuel Richardson's *Pamela*, the first genuine English novel, was published in 1740, when English drama was weak. Such novelists as Henry Fielding and Tobias Smollett (both writing in the eighteenth century) and Charles Dickens (writing in the nineteenth century) sometimes wrote novels with a string of actions unified only through the hero's participation in those actions. Each action did not necessarily have a purpose, as it might in drama. The novelists Jane Austen (1775-1817) and Emily Brontë (1818-1848) emphasized character inseparable from plot rather than scattered actions. Their characters are influenced by actions, and act in ways that influence plot. Henry James (1843-1916) examined character further by revealing characters' thoughts and motivations.

A novelist is not always clear in explaining their own processes of writing. Yet, there are oftentimes similarities between successful novelists.

Authors must write about subjects that align with their experience, understanding, ability, and temperament. Writers must be critical in selecting material for novels; they must include only those actions, events, descriptive details, gestures, and structures that unify that huge work to produce a meaningful vision to the reader. They should recognize limits in experience and ability. Jane Austen probably knew that she should not attempt to describe a battlefield (about which she knew little), but she could portray human cruelty realistically in everyday situations.

Even though successful novelist have a purpose in writing a novel, they do not limit writing to a narrow point of view; that approach would only produce propaganda. The vast size of the novel enables them to present social, political, or religious theories and developments in all their stages and interpretations so that intelligent readers can understand the complexity of situations and can choose approaches after careful thought. An honest novelist should not advocate solutions but should contemplate and educate.

Answer *true* or *false*.

3.122	_____	The novel has been a respected literary form for four hundred years.
3.123	_____	Some ancient and medieval works have several qualities present in novels.
3.124	_____	The first genuine English novel *Pamela* was published in 1840.
3.125	_____	Charles Dickens wrote the first English novel.
3.126	_____	The nineteenth century reading public enjoyed novels.
3.127	_____	Charles Dickens wrote some novels in which actions are only unified through the heroes' participation in those actions.
3.128	_____	The novel has continued drama's function of showing characters in action.
3.129	_____	Emily Brontë's characters are inseparable from plot.
3.130	_____	Jane Austen's novels are usually a string of loosely connected actions.

3.131 _____ A novelist should be able to handle any subject.

3.132 _____ A novel is big enough to hold any material the novelist wants to include.

3.133 _____ Jane Austen probably knew that she was too inexperienced to write about wars.

3.134 _____ A novelist should limit writing to a narrow point of view.

A novel may be distinctive in its type; it may be a novel of manners (dealing with the customs and values of a specific social class), a novel of character, a historical novel, a detective novel, or a science-fiction novel (a more complete list may be found in Language Arts 1009, Section 2). Most worthwhile novels, however, have several elements in common. The following list should enable you to review the elements of the novel in general, and to reconsider Charles Sheldon's novel, *In His Steps*, in particular.

1. *Plot* is "a series of planned interrelated actions that progress through a struggle of forces that oppose one another until a climax and resolution are reached" (Language Arts 1009). These actions must be logically planned, must be in a series, and must have conflict. They must also be selected and simplified so that the novel becomes a unified work of art. In a good novel, logical actions come naturally from the characters.

2. *Characterization*, the creation of imaginary persons that are believable in their fictional world, is another important element in the novel. Main characters should probably be well rounded personalities, combinations of physical traits, significant actions, and revealing ideas. These characters may develop or become educated during the course of the novel, a process that usually is not possible in short stories. Minor characters, however, may simply have a dominant trait that may provide conflict or that may serve some other function in the novel. A novelist usually uses one of, or a combination of, the following methods to characterize:

   a. The author can *tell* the reader what to think about the character by *explaining* the character's traits and actions.

   b. The author can present the character's actions and permit the reader to make up his own mind about the character.

   c. The author can reveal the character's thoughts, usually through point of view.

3. *Imagery* and *symbols* recreate experience for the reader and provide several levels of meaning so that the novel becomes an individual experience for each reader.

   a. An *image* is "a literal and concrete representation of an *experience* of the *senses* or of an *object* that can be known by...the senses" (Language Arts 1009).

   b. A *symbol* is something that stands for something else but has a literal identity as well. In the novel, *In His Steps*, the Rectangle is a symbol of earthly poverty.

4. *Setting* and its *atmosphere* or *mood* should provide the *background* for the characters in action, unless the book emphasizes travel and is not concerned with characters. Descriptive details used in creating the atmosphere or mood should probably have some relationship to the characters so that the novel will remain unified. In the novel, *In His Steps*, Maxwell's view of the atmosphere in the Rectangle reveals aspects of his character.

Answer the following questions.

3.135 What is a novel of manners? _____

_____

3.136 How would a travel book differ from a novel of character? _____

_____

3.137 How do you describe the plot of a good novel? _____

_____

3.138 How might a character change in the course of a novel? _____

_____

_____

3.139 How might a novelist use a character with just one dominant trait? _____

_____

3.140 How will a successful novelist use setting to unify a novel? _____

_____

3.141 In the novel, *In His Steps*, of what is the Rectangle a symbol? _____

_____

3.142 What two elements are most important in a novel? _____

_____

3.143 What are three methods used in characterization?

a. _____

b. _____

c. _____

Complete the following activity.

3.144 Reviewing these qualities of a good novel and writing a literary critique for Section 1 of this LIFEPAC should have enabled you to form definite opinions about the novel you read, *In His Steps*. Once again, ask yourself these questions. (You may also refer back to the notes you took in Language Arts 1009 and to the book review written in Section 3.)

This final exercise should help you to understand that an accurate evaluation of a piece of writing takes careful study and much time.

a. What is the purpose of this novel? _____

b. Did Sheldon achieve this purpose? _____

c. How does this novel contribute to your understanding of human nature?

_____

_____

_____

_____

d. What elements enable you to enjoy this novel (or prevent you from enjoying it)?

_____

e. What is its greatest strength? _____

_____

f. What is its greatest weakness? _____

_____

g. Are you most impressed with its strengths or weaknesses? _____

_____

h. Are these conclusions consistent with the ideas in your book review written at the conclusion of Language Arts 1009?

_____

i. If your opinions have changed somewhat, how do you explain this change?

_____

_____

TEACHER CHECK _____ _____

initials   date

Before you take this last Self Test, you may want to do one or more of these self checks.

1. _____ Read the objectives. See if you can do them.

2. _____ Restudy the material related to any objectives that you cannot do.

3. _____ Use the **SQ3R** study procedure to review the material.

    a. **S**can the sections.

    b. **Q**uestion yourself.

    c. **R**ead to answer your questions.

    d. **R**ecite the answers to yourself.

    e. **R**eview areas you did not understand.

4. _____ Review all vocabulary, activities, and Self Tests, writing a correct answer for every wrong answer.

SELF TEST 3

Answer *true* **or** *false* (each answer, 1 point).

3.01 _____ When preparing literature for an oral interpretation, you should select a passage with much description or narration.

3.02 _____ The marks /, //, >, < are standard for marking pauses and emphasis in a speech.

3.03 _____ If you are stiff and too nervous to look at your audience during your speech, take a few steps and look slightly above your audience.

3.04 _____ Adjectives used in a paper should be necessary and specific.

3.05 _____ *Informal*, *general*, and *formal* are terms describing levels of standard English usage.

3.06 _____ Connotations are word endings that indicate the grammatical functions of words.

3.07 _____ An etymology is a syntax of a word.

3.08 _____ Nonrestrictive clauses are unnecessary to the meaning of the words modified and are set off by commas.

3.09 _____ As you listen to a speaker, you should evaluate evidence by deciding whether the argument is supported by facts or just with opinions.

3.010 _____ In a speech, difficult words are often helpful in getting an audience's interest.

Match these items (each answer, 2 points).

3.011 _____ a word for which a pronoun stands

3.012 _____ verbals used only as adjectives

3.013 _____ verbals ending in *-ing* and used only as nouns

3.014 _____ contains at least two independent clauses

3.015 _____ time sequence

3.016 _____ supported with examples

3.017 _____ the arrangement of beats or accents in a line of poetry

3.018 _____ the pattern in which similar end-sounds occur in a poem

3.019 _____ the use of words that sound like the noises they describe

3.020 _____ the repetition of consonants at the beginning of words (baa, baa, black sheep)

a. participles

b. compound sentence

c. antecedent

d. illustrative texts

e. gerunds

f. rhyme scheme

g. onomatopoeia

h. chronological order

i. alliteration

j. apostrophe

k. meter

Write the letter of the correct answer on each line (each answer, 2 points)

3.021 Sayings that have lost their meaning through overuse are _____ .
a. connotations   b. clichés   c. inflections   d. gerunds

3.022 Recipes, instruction sheets, and "How to" articles are types of _____ .
a. illustrative texts   b. process essay
c. classification texts   d. literary critiques

3.023 The suggestive meanings or atmospheres of a word are its _____ .
a. etymologies   b. inflections   c. denotations   d. connotations

3.024 An example of a logical sentence is " _____ ".
a. Good grades are never an indication of someone's success in the real world
b. Students who are good athletes are not musically talented
c. Milk is usually an important food for babies
d. We always have rain on Easter Sunday

3.025 The term that does *not* name a metric foot is _____ .
a. anapestic   b. trochaic   c. iambic   d. hexameter

3.026 The term that tells us that a line of poetry has five feet is _____ .
a. pentameter   b. heptameter   c. dactylic   d. odometer

3.027 Plays that include events of the Old and New Testaments and incidents in the lives of saints are _____ .
a. morality plays   b. miracle plays   c. comedies   d. mimes

3.028 The element that is *not* usually found in a tragedy is _____ .
a. a flaw in the hero   b. action that produces a catharsis
c. suffering hero   d. pantomimes and Latin dialogue

3.029 A drama should have *all* of these *three* elements: _____ .
a. characters impersonated by actors, a monologue, and a soliloquy
b. a plot, an aside, and an allegory
c. dialogue, plot, and dramatic irony
d. dialogue, plot, and characters impersonated by actors

3.030 Everyman enters the grave with _____ .
a. Goods   b. Fellowship   c. Good Deeds   d. Kindred

Complete these statements (each answer, 2 points).

3.031 A struggle taking place within the protagonist is called an internal _____ .

3.032 The rising action ends and the reader experiences the greatest emotional impact of the story at the _____ of the story.

3.033 The main character of a short story is sometimes called the _____ .

3.034 In the story "The Celebrated Jumping Frog of Calaveras County," the character _____ tells the narrator about Jim Smiley and his frog Dan'l Webster.

3.035 A story within a story is a(n) _____ .

3.036 An image is a(n) a. _____ and b. _____ representation of an experience of the senses or of an object that can be known by the senses.

3.037 "The Celebrated Jumping Frog of Calaveras County" was written by _____ .

3.038 The first genuine English novel, _____ , was written by Samuel Richardson and published in 1740.

3.039 The novel has continued drama's function of showing _____ .

3.040 In the novel, *In His Steps*, _____ is a symbol of earthly poverty.

Answer these questions (each answer, 2 points).

3.041 What are two ways in which a speech can be made suitable
for a particular kind of audience?

a. _____

b. _____

3.042 What are four ways to read for meaning?

a. _____

b. _____

c. _____

d. _____

3.043 What are the five elements most short stories have in common?

a. _____

b. _____

c. _____

d. _____

e. _____

3.044 What are three methods of characterization a novelist may use?

a. _____

b. _____

c. _____

80 / 100   **SCORE** _____   **TEACHER** _____ _____
                                                   initials   date

Before taking the LIFEPAC Test, you may want to do one or more of these self checks.
1. _____ Read the objectives. See if you can do them.
2. _____ Restudy the material related to any objectives that you cannot do.
3. _____ Use the **SQ3R** study procedure to review the material.
4. _____ Review activities, Self Tests, and LIFEPAC vocabulary words.
5. _____ Restudy areas of weakness indicated by the last Self Test.

GLOSSARY

alliteration .... The repetition of consonants which appear at the beginning of words (*b*aa, *b*aa, *b*lack sheep).

antecedent .... A word for which a pronoun stands.

appositive .... A noun, pronoun, or phrase that follows another noun or pronoun to explain it, and is grammatically the same.

chronological sequence .... Ordered according to time, in order of occurrence.

clichés .... Phrases which have lost their meaning through overuse.

concrete images .... Objects that can be known by one or more of the five senses.

connectives .... Words or phrases that connect words, phrases, or paragraphs. Examples include transitions, conjunctions, pronouns, and key words.

connotation .... Suggestive meaning or atmosphere of a word.

coordinating conjunction .... A conjunction which joins *equal* elements, such as two independent clauses or two verbs.

etymology .... The history of a word.

expository writing .... Writing which explains rather than describes, narrates a story, or argues a point; six types are often recognized: cause and effect, definition, classification, process analysis, comparison or contrast, and illustration or example.

frame story .... A story within a story; the overall narrator describes and presents a second storyteller.

illustrative essay .... An essay which has a thesis supported with examples.

inflections .... Word endings indicating grammatical function.

intensive .... A pronoun ending in -*self* and emphasizing by immediate repetition the previously used noun or pronoun.

levels of usage .... Formal, semi-formal, and informal (or colloquial), all three levels are forms of standard English usage.

logical fallacies .... False acts of reasoning.

miracle play .... A medieval play describing events of the Old and New Testaments and stories about saints.

morality play	A medieval play that is a dramatized allegory in which virtues and vices struggle for man's soul.
nonrestrictive clauses	Clauses unnecessary to the meaning of the words modified; they are set off by commas.
onomatopoeia	The use of words that sound like the noises they describe.
optimum pitch	The level at which the voice operates with the greatest ease.
pitch	Tone; the highness and lowness of the voice.
point of view	The position from which the author presents the story (usually first person or third person).
process analysis	Recipes, instruction sheets, and "How to" articles are all examples of this type of essay which explains a process, usually in chronological order.
reflexive	A pronoun ending in -*self* and referring to the previously used noun or pronoun.
resonance	Amplification of the voice.
restrictive clause	A clause necessary to the meaning of the word modified; it is not set off by commas.
rhyme scheme	The pattern in which similar end-sounds (or rhymes) occur in a poem.
suffix	A unit of meaning added at the end of a word.
syntax	Fixed word order.
theme	The central idea in a literary work.
tragic hero	The main character who suffers a turn in fortune because of his tragic flaw.
verbal	A verb form that functions as a noun or a modifier while retaining the characteristics of a verb. There are three types: participles, infinitives, and gerunds.

LANGUAGE ARTS 1010

LIFEPAC TEST

NAME _____

DATE _____

SCORE _____

Answer *true* **or** *false* (each answer, 1 point).

1. _____ If you are stiff and too nervous to look at your audience during your speech, take a few steps and stare at the floor.

2. _____ As you listen to a speaker, you should evaluate his evidence by deciding whether or not they are a qualified authority on his topic.

3. _____ In a speech, difficult words should be defined or avoided.

4. _____ Sayings that have lost their meaning through overuse are connotations.

5. _____ The suggestive meanings or atmospheres of a word are its inflections.

6. _____ A metric foot marked ˘ ′ is iambic.

7. _____ A tragedy often has a tragic hero who suffers because of his flawed character.

8. _____ Everyman enters the grave with Goods.

9. _____ At the climax of a story, the rising action ends and the reader experiences the greatest emotional impact of the story.

10. _____ Dan'l Webster was a frog.

Match these items (each answer, 2 points).

11. _____ word endings that indicate the grammatical functions of words

12. _____ the history of a word

13. _____ informal, semi-formal, formal

14. _____ clauses unnecessary to the meaning of the words modified, set off by commas

15. _____ time sequence

16. _____ supported with examples

17. _____ recipes, instruction sheets, "How to" articles

18. _____ five metric feet

19. _____ main character

20. _____ a story within a story

a. levels of usage

b. restrictive

c. chronological order

d. pentameter

e. inflections

f. illustrative essay

g. etymology

h. protagonist

i. nonrestrictive

j. process analysis

k. frame

Write the letter of the correct answer on each line (each answer, 2 points).

21. Adjectives used in a paper should be _____ .
    a. general and numerous
    b. specific and numerous
    c. necessary and general
    d. necessary and specific

22. When preparing literature for an oral interpretation, you should _____ .
    a. select several short passages to paste together
    b. select a key passage that can stand alone
    c. select a passage with much description and narration
    d. select a passage with as many characters as possible

23. A struggle taking place within the protagonist is _____ .
    a. external conflict   b. a personification
    c. an antagonist   d. an internal conflict

24. In the story, "The Celebrated Jumping Frog of Calaveras County," the character _____ tells the narrator about Smiley and his frog.
    a. Dan'l Webster   b. Andrew Jackson   c. Simon Wheeler   d. the stranger

25. A novel of manners deals with _____ .
    a. plot   b. customs   c. characters   d. setting

26. A speech can be made suitable for a particular audience by _____ .
   a. using clichés and formal diction
   b. using recordings and breathing exercises
   c. using an interesting subject, a suitable level of usage, and words with appropriate connotations
   d. using words with suitable connotations, difficult words, and gestures

27. The arrangement of beats or accents in a line of poetry is _____ .
   a. rhyme   b. meter   c. alliteration   d. apostrophe

28. The first genuine English novel, *Pamela*, was written by Samuel Richardson and published in _____ .
   a. 1740   b. 1340   c. 1640   d. 1940

29. The novel showed characters in action and continued the tradition and function of _____ .
   a. poetry   b. short stories   c. drama   d. science fiction

30. In the novel, *In His Step*s, the Rectangle is a(n) _____ .
   a. image   b. character   c. miracle play   d. symbol

Complete these statements (each answer, 3 points).

31. The marks /, //, (word) are standard for marking _____ _____ .

32. A word for which a pronoun stands is its _____ .

33. Verbals ending in *-ing* and used only as nouns are _____ .

34. Verbals used only as adjectives are _____ .

35. The sentence, "Students who are good athletes are not musically talented," is _____ .

36. Plays that include events of the Old and New Testaments and incidents in the lives of saints are _____ .

37. A sentence that contains one independent clause and at least one dependent clause is a(n) _____ .

38. The pattern in which similar end-sounds occur in a poem is that poem's _____ .

39. The repetition of consonants at the beginning of words (*baa*, *baa*, black sheep) is _____ .

40. The use of words that sound like the noises they describe is _____ .

Answer these questions (each question, 5 points).

41. What are three elements a drama should have?

    a. _____

    b. _____

    c. _____

42. What are the five elements most short stories have in common?

    a. _____

    b. _____

    c. _____

    d. _____

    e. _____

43. What are four ways to read for meaning?

    a. _____

    b. _____

    c. _____

    d. _____

44. What are three methods of characterization a novelist may use?

    a. _____

    _____

    b. _____

    _____

    c. _____

    _____